A Philosophy
of Ground Control

A Philosophy of Ground Control

A Bridge Between Theory and Practice

R. G. K. MORRISON

Department of Mining and
Metallurgical Engineering,
McGill University

MONTREAL   1976

First published 1970 by Ontario Department of Mines
Revised and enlarged edition published 1976

© Department of Mining and Metallurgical Engineering,
McGill University 1976.

Legal deposit third quarter 1976
Bibliothèque nationale du Quebec

ISBN   0-9690582-0-9

Design by Anthony Crouch MGDC

Printed and bound in Canada by
T. H. Best Printing Company.

Contents

Plates

Preface

I first became interested in ground control as a result of operating experience on the Kolar Gold Field, South India. I arrived there shortly before the departure of J. S. Jones, a physicist of outstanding ability, who was completing a six-year study of problems associated with ventilation and ground pressure. At that time the Kolar Gold Field was one of the few deep mining areas of the world and consequently such problems were of a pioneering nature. It speaks well for the managers of the operating companies, Messrs. John Taylor & Sons, London, that they had the foresight to seek early scientific advice on these problems. Perhaps my earliest contribution was in the recognition that some of Jones' ideas on ground control had a place in the operational context.

Mining is an industry where good judgement, often most conspicuous in hindsight, carries a greater premium than in most other industries. The fundamentals of good judgement are knowledge and experience. These notes are offered as a contribution to that objective. They were prepared as a background for lecture material during the period when I was a member of the staff of the Department of Mining Engineering and Applied Geophysics at McGill University. They arise from some personal knowledge of the world's deeper mining areas and also from exposure to the problems of many other mining operations.

It is a pleasure to record the assistance of Drs. D. F. Coates, L. P. Geldart and J. E. G. Schwellnus, former members of the McGill Faculty, as well as that of Dr. D. G. F. Hedley, of CANMET, Department of Energy, Mines, and Resources, Canada. I am also indebted to my graduate students for constructive criticism; some of their contributions have been recorded by the National Academy of Sciences, Washington, D.C. (1) and others appear in the list of references.

A number of the illustrations have been supplied through the kindness of Algoma Steel Corporation Limited, The International Nickel Company of Canada Limited, and Gaspé Copper Mines Limited. I am indebted to these and other companies for useful data. Thanks are also due to the Canadian Institute of Mining and Metallurgy for permission to reproduce references 58 and 59.

I have been greatly assisted in the preparation of this second edition by my colleagues Professors B. W. Mackenzie, J. E. Udd, and W. M. Williams. Their help is gratefully acknowledged. Finally it is a pleasure to acknowledge the services of Miss Ruth Griffith who typed the manuscript of this edition.

R. G. K. Morrison
EMERITUS PROFESSOR OF MINING
ENGINEERING, MCGILL UNIVERSITY

Foreword   TO THE FIRST EDITION

This is published at a time when growing interest is being displayed in mining methods and ground control in an expanding mining industry. I recommend the use of this monograph as a textbook for the operators, engineers and scientists in the industry involved in making analytical observations concerned with the subject and the safety of the workmen in the winning of mineral resources.

Professor R.G.K. Morrison, formerly Head of the Department of Mining Engineering and Applied Geophysics, McGill University, has consistently been a leader in the development of studies arising from the need to break and remove rock or ore while maintaining control over the surrounding rock. He has studied the complex problems associated with mining methods and ground control throughout the world as an operator, scientist, professor and consulting engineer. He writes with authority and publication of his manuscript recognizes an outstanding career and will acquaint those involved with rock problems of the need and practicability of applying engineering principles.

HON. ALLAN F. LAWRENCE, Q.C.,
Minister of Mines.

ONTARIO DEPARTMENT OF MINES,
TORONTO, ONTARIO.
1970

Foreword

Professor R. G. K. Morrison, with a unique combination of experiences, has provided the Canadian mining industry for forty years with guidance on deep mining. For twenty-five years he worked through most positions around a mine from operations to management, including the supervision of some of the deepest operations in the world — The Kolar Gold Field — in South India. Also at various times there was exposure to ground problems in South Africa, U.S.A., United Kingdom, Brazil, and numerous operations in Canada.

As a mining consultant, his early work for the Ontario Mining Association became a classical reference on the avoidance of rockbursts. Arising with this work the International Nickel Company of Canada Limited sponsored the production of a film that demonstrated Professor Morrison's ideas on the development of stress concentrations associated with stoping. The successful combination of theory and practice was demonstrated by the utilization of that film for a longer period of time than any Hollywood best seller.

As a professor, he was Chairman of the Department of Mining Engineering and Applied Geophysics at McGill University at a time when the training of mining engineers was in a state of considerable flux. Based on his knowledge of mining and men, he knew that the best combination for a practical education was to be obtained by emphasizing studies in the basic sciences combined with field experience in operating mines. He guided the department well during this difficult period.

When he decided upon a university career he had no intention of leaving advances in mining to others. His orientation was that he knew substantially all that the practical man knew about ground control. Admitting that this was less than desirable, he wanted to explore the possibilities of a theoretical approach and so initiated the first rock mechanics research program in Canada at McGill University. Over a period of two decades he attracted a large number of outstanding postgraduate students, not only from Canada, but from the United Kingdom, South Africa, India, and other countries. Much useful scientific work was done in this program on studying rock properties and the analysis of stress around mine openings (1).

While on the McGill faculty myself, I was drawn into the rock mechanics program as a result of Professor Morrison demonstrating the challenge and intellectual opportunities that existed. Through the good offices of Mr. Carl Beck and the generosity of Algoma Ore Properties, Professor Morrison was able to obtain a research grant that permitted me to do some work on stress concentrations and rockbursts which led to our joint presentation at the first rock mechanics session to be sponsored by the Canadian Institute of Mining and Metallurgy, at the Annual Meeting in 1955. Subsequent to that Professor Morrison drew me into the work of the Special Committee on Mining Practices at Elliot Lake, commissioned by the Minister of Mines, Ontario, in 1958. This permitted me to make some early contribution to the understanding of the stability of pillars.

With advances in the subject of rock mechanics, it was eventually felt that some of the theoretical work could be exposed to the mining fraternity. With the offer by Professor Morrison and McGill University of sponsorship and with the assistance of the Mines Branch through Mr. Alex Ignatieff and Dr. John Convey, and The International Nickel Company of Canada Limited through Mr. R. D. Parker, the First Canadian Rock Mechanics Symposium was conducted in 1962. This started a series of symposia sponsored, in subsequent years, by different universities and the CIM, with the Tenth symposium held in 1975. The record thus testifies to the large contribution that Professor Morrison has made to the improvement of Canadian mining practices.

In summarizing his experience in this extensively revised edition of *A Philosophy of Ground Control* Professor Morrison examines in some detail the points upon which good judgement and the state of the art now depend. He also offers explanations for most observations bearing on ground control that might be made by a shift boss as he travels his beat.

This revised edition is published by the Department of Mining and Metallurgical Engineering in support of the Mining Scholarship Fund of McGill University. It will be a useful reference to all operating engineers and particularly to those wishing to bridge the gap between theory and practice in matters relating to ground control.

D. F. Coates,

Director-General, Canada Centre
for Mineral and Energy Technology,
Department of Energy, Mines & Resources,
Ottawa, Canada.

Introduction

The effect of unpredicted ground failure due to mining is reflected in many ways. In surface mining the safe slope of open pit walls is a matter of great economic importance. Falls of ground are perhaps the greatest single cause of underground mining fatalities; costly surface damage has resulted from subsidence; shafts and other mine openings have been lost or damaged due to stresses imposed by subsequent mining operations; mines have been flooded due to rock failure under large bodies of water or under water-bearing strata; low-cost mining methods have had to be replaced by more costly methods because of accidents, dilution, and loss of ore resulting from ground failure; wall closure in stopes and its reflection on levels through mined areas and also the maintenance of travelling ways through unmined ground may demand costly alternatives. The foregoing types of failure are gradual to the extent that there is usually some prior warning, if it can be observed. Superimposed on these is the less common but more dangerous sudden type of failure in the form of a rockburst.

Many of these phenomena are accompanied by increased accident risk, higher costs, and loss of ore to a degree which demands that we know more about their specific causes. Fortunately, in practice, these are the exceptional cases but until they become completely predictable we are not masters of the situation.

The miner, in living with such problems over the years, has developed empirical rules to ensure better control, and, when possible, predictability. While trial and error methods cannot be dispensed with, it is realized that the most reliable control can be achieved only through a better knowledge of the range and limitations of the many variables involved. The scientist, not necessarily concerned with economic aspects, is now prominent in the picture and a science of rock mechanics has developed with its practical applications directed towards the study of causes, prediction, and control of rock failure as related to problems of mine and open pit design and the comminution of rocks including drilling and blasting. It is an extension of the spectrum of soil mechanics into the field of the more cohesive sedimentary, igneous, and metamorphic rocks.

The acceptability of the scientific approach depends upon how accurately it can simulate conditions to be observed in practice. This introduces an interdependence between scientist and operator in the selection of principles which are of value in developing a working knowledge of cause and effect. These principles, often obscured by local conditions, represent the common threads which weave their way

The George W. MacLeod Mine of the Algoma Steel Corporation Limited at Wawa, Ontario. The illustration looks eastward where the western section of the siderite orebody, 250' in width and dipping 70° to the south has been mined for a strike length of 1500' to a depth also of about 1500'. Support consists of only a few unmined dikes and fault displacements and slough from the walls. Several hundreds of feet of natural waste slough cover operations below, but it is of interest to observe that only a portion of the hangingwall, unsupported by slough, has worked back through tensile failure to form a vertical face as shown. (*Courtesy of Algoma Steel Corporation Limited*)

through most problems in ground control. The more obvious are related to the physical properties and structure of rock masses and their reactions to stress concentrations arising with the geometry of openings. The relationship can be visualized as a strength / stress ratio and the critical stress can be either tensile or compressive.

Rock failure as observed in mines represents a local strength / stress ratio of somewhat less than 1:1 in either tension or compression and variations from this cannot be expressed in absolute values at the present time. We look to the scientific approach to improve this situation. It relies on measurements in the mine, model studies and theory, occasionally based upon complicated mathematics. The practical operator, in his judgement, depends upon trends suggested by such studies and thus requires some knowledge of their limitations. Within this context more rigorous analytical methods are readily available (2, 3). However, they must be used with caution as the field stress pattern and the structure and properties of the rock mass are seldom reduced to acceptable working values. Good judgement thus depends upon a judicious blending of the practical with the theoretical.

In the competition between the art and the science in mining, the art still appears to be in command, but in quantifying trends (4) science has added much to our understanding of ground problems. It is reasonable to assume that in time science will encroach further upon the art and improve predictability accordingly.

In the following pages most ideas bearing on decision-making in ground control are touched upon and mathematical solutions are occasionally introduced as background material but they are not essential for the interpretation of the text.

1 | Rocks and Rock Masses

The Physical Properties of Rocks

The petrographer, for purposes of identification and comparison, has classified rocks on the basis of origin, mineral content, and grain or crystallographic structure. In addition to this, the miner requires a classification based on physical properties and behaviour under stress. This implies some knowledge of rock properties in compression, tension, and shear, under the numerous conditions of loading which can apply and also of the various environmental factors influencing the strength / stress relationship such as confinement, time, temperature, moisture content, and structural conditions of the rock mass.

The literature provides data on many rock properties derived from unconfined compression, torsion, tension, and shear tests. In such tests the tensile strength ranges well below the shearing strength which, in turn, is usually a small fraction of the compressive strength. In biaxial and triaxial tests, strength increases with increasing confinement and in mining, some degree of confinement is usually present. We know also that in the deformation and rupture of rocks, the effects of elasticity, plasticity, and viscosity may be apparent (5, 6) and the latter are more prominent under differentially confined conditions.

For the present very general purposes, elasticity will be considered as covering those conditions of deformation within the state of recoverable strain. This goes somewhat beyond classical elasticity, which conforms with Hooke's Law that stress is proportional to strain, to include strains developed and / or recoverable over a period of time. We can then regard viscosity and plasticity as including all non-recoverable states of strain including rupture (7).

ELASTICITY

Classical elasticity obeys Hooke's Law, "Stress is proportional to strain."

Thus $\Delta \ell$ = unit linear deformation = $\dfrac{P}{E}$

P = stress

E = Young's modulus

Classical elasticity represents a completely reversible (frictionless) process capable of storing free potential energy, and deformation is an instantaneous function of stress. It can be represented graphically by the straight line stress / strain curve of figure 1 which holds for both the loading and unloading cycles.

FIGURE 1

Stress Strain Diagram
Hooke's Law

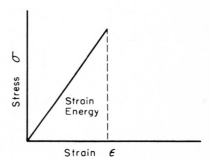

The temperature-dependence of elasticity is illustrated by the case of a steel spring (potential elasticity) and a gas (kinetic elasticity due to the energy of its molecules). With increasing temperature the former softens and the latter stiffens. Ideal elasticity is limited to a certain temperature range and / or condition of loading.

For the purpose of rheological models Hooke's elasticity (H) is represented by a coil spring, figure 2:

FIGURE 2

Elastic Behaviour

In an infinite, homogeneous, and isotropic medium complying with Hooke's Law, the elastic constants are related as follows:

$$G = \frac{E}{2(1 + \gamma)} \qquad\qquad 1$$

$$B = \frac{E}{3(1 - 2\gamma)} \qquad\qquad 2$$

$$\frac{V}{v} = \frac{2(1-\gamma)}{1-2\gamma} \qquad\qquad 3$$

$$V = \frac{E(1-\gamma)}{d(1+\gamma)(1-2\gamma)} \qquad\qquad 4$$

G = modulus of rigidity (shear modulus)
E = Young's modulus = stress / longitudinal strain
γ = Poisson's ratio = lateral strain / longitudinal strain
B = bulk modulus (the reciprocal of cubic compressibility)
V = longitudinal velocity of sound waves
v = transverse velocity of sound waves
d = density

It is apparent that if the density and any two of the above constants are known, the remainder can be calculated within the assumption of perfect elasticity. For incompressible materials B = infinity, γ = 0.5, and E = 3G.

Elastic moduli may be determined either by dynamic or by static methods. For dynamic methods a sonic procedure has been described by the U.S. Bureau of Mines (8). This provides for the measurements of the fundamental longitudinal and torsional frequency of vibration in a test specimen. From this data Young's modulus and the modulus of rigidity may be calculated permitting a solution of the above formulae.

In the static methods the longitudinal and lateral deformation of a test specimen are measured under uniaxial loading to give Young's modulus and Poisson's ratio. The modulus of rigidity may be obtained from torsion tests.

Dynamic methods usually give higher values than static methods for Young's modulus of rocks, and particularly so in the low pressure range. The difference is attributed to internal friction in anelastic solids (9).

The elastic constants as applied to rocks have a wide application in geophysics. In the narrower field of mine design, however, their value depends upon their constancy which in turn indicates the degree to which the theory of elasticity is valid in any particular case. They have a comparative value in assessing the probable behaviour of rock types under mining conditions. Also, in measuring stress in rocks *in situ*, the conversion of strain measurements into stress units depends, in part, on the accuracy of the determination of Young's modulus and Poisson's ratio as related to the specific strain measurements. Here it is to be noted that values for these moduli can be varied both with the load and with the method of determination. Their use in converting strain measurements into stress estimates thus still requires caution.

PLASTICITY

In these notes plasticity represents a non-recoverable deformation or flow, usually without obvious fracture, in an otherwise elastic body. It is initiated by shearing stresses above a critical level or yield value and continues under constant load.

Should the load fall below this yield value, deformation ceases and some elastic recovery may follow. Plasticity varies from classical viscosity in that the energy dissipation is more dependent on the yield value than on the rate of deformation. Neglecting any purely elastic deformation, the condition is shown graphically in figure 3.

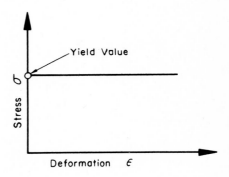

FIGURE 3

Stress-Deformation Diagram
Plastic Behaviour

For rheological models, the mechanical behaviour of such a (St. Venant) solid is represented by a weight pulled against friction by a Hooke spring as in figure 4.

FIGURE 4

Model of
Plastic Behaviour

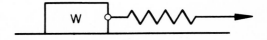

In applied mechanics (10) plastic materials are those whose shear resistance is independent of the degree of deformation.

VISCOSITY

When the deformation of a body continues indefinitely under the action of a finite force it is said to flow. Viscosity defines the behaviour of such a material in terms of stress and velocity strain (rate of strain). As compared with the threshold or yield value of plastic flow, viscous flow occurs under the action of any force. The rate of flow is dependent on and vanishes with the force. The energy dissipated in producing a given deformation depends upon the rate of deformation. Ideally viscous flow is represented by the Newtonian liquid (N) where:

$$\Delta = P / n \text{ or } P = n\frac{(du)}{(dt)}$$

where Δ = unit time deformation = $\dfrac{du}{dt}$

P = shearing stress
n = coefficient of viscosity

The concept of viscosity is shown graphically in figure 5.

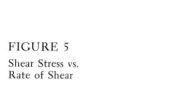

FIGURE 5

Shear Stress vs.
Rate of Shear

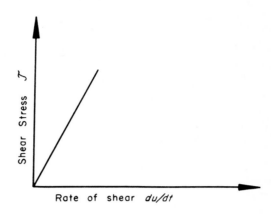

For rheological models viscosity is represented by a dash pot, an undersized piston being drawn through a viscous liquid as in figure 6.

FIGURE 6

Dashpot Model of
Viscous Behaviour

THE BURGER MODEL

The Hooke solid and the Newtonian liquid are abstractions. Nevertheless, they help to understand the very complex relationships between the time-dependent deformations which are physical realities with rocks.

The deformation of solids under load represents some combination of effects associated with elasticity, plasticity and / or viscosity. Test work on rocks suggests an analogy with the Burger model shown in figure 7 in which A represents an elastic element, B a recoverable time strain and C a permanent deformation. The model may be compared with stress / strain curves given later.

Non-recoverable deformation such as creep, flow, and rupture present problems in practical mining. They can influence the stress pattern around mine openings, and when resisted may result in stress concentrations. Normally, however, they have the advantage of being related to a time factor and to the dissipation of strain energy.

Our earlier, rather loose definition for non-recoverable strain, which may or may not represent loss of cohesion, covers the numerous possibilities included under combinations of plasticity, viscosity, and internal friction, and obviously requires

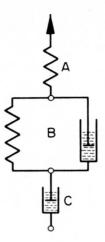

FIGURE 7

The Burger Model

further study. Apparent examples in mines, except for the flow of clay-like material, usually involve shearing and loss of cohesion. Both in laboratory work and in practice the dividing line between recoverable time-dependent elasticity, and non-recoverable plasticity and viscosity in mine rocks has not been clearly defined and the distinction may well trace back to molecular and atomic bonding.

Laboratory tests with the harder rock types suggest that on unloading, most of the strain is recoverable within a few hours and the remainder has been regarded as permanent set. There are also geological grounds for believing that under high confining pressure the amount of permanent set in rocks is related to a time factor, the inference being that with a sufficiently low rate of loading over geological time the reaction would be entirely plastic with no recoverable strain. Some geological structures suggest this characteristic. On the other hand, the lack of agreement as to the long term nature of time-dependent strains, elastic, plastic or viscous, under various environmental conditions offers an interesting field for research. In the final analysis, however, all can be accepted as rock properties. Strains in the earth's crust, in addition to those due to gravity loading, must be ascribed to loading history or to other tectonic causes.

Nadai's work (11) on plasticity is also an excellent reference, but the plastic problem in mines, while present in varying degree, is not well understood. Rockbursts, concerned with the sudden release of strain energy, have offered the most conspicuous challenge to the industry and it is thus natural to emphasize the theory of elasticity in examining problems of failure in hard rocks.

STRESS-STRAIN RELATIONSHIPS

The stress-strain diagrams indicate varying rock characteristics. Figure 8, after D. W. Phillips (12), shows both elastic and plastic deformation during the uniaxial loading of a coal measure shale. Figure 9 for the same specimen shows time deforma-

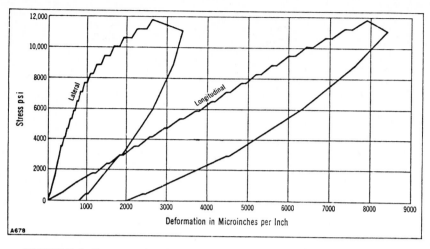

FIGURE 8 Stress-strain characteristics of a coal-measure shale; load applied in increments at 10-minute intervals (*After D. W. Phillips*[12])

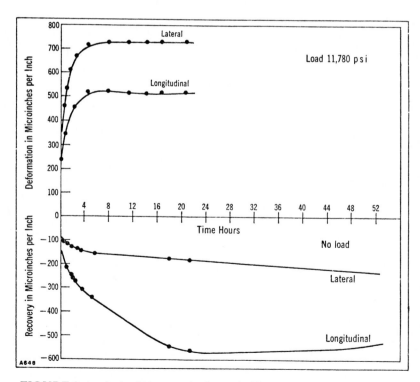

FIGURE 9 Analysis of time-strain shown in Figure 8 at full load (11,780) and upon removal of load, showing time recovery (*After D. W. Phillips*[12])

tion and time recovery respectively, at full load and when unloaded. A large plastic deformation or permanent set remained 20 hours after removal of load.

Figure 10 shows an elastic reaction very nearly to the point of rupture for a Witwatersrand quartzite under uniaxial load. Some plasticity develops short of rupture (13).

Figure 11 is at the other extreme and shows the visco-elastic reaction of salt from the hangingwall of the potash beds in Saskatchewan (14). Had the specimen been unloaded prior to failure some of the deformation would have remained as a permanent set, as in figure 8. Potash has similar characteristics.

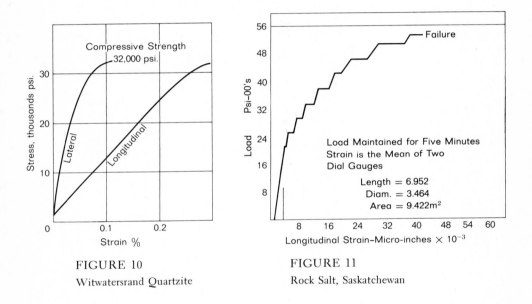

FIGURE 10

Witwatersrand Quartzite

FIGURE 11

Rock Salt, Saskatchewan

Figure 12 shows the uniaxial loading and unloading cycle for a Porcupine dacite (15). The hysteresis loop between loading and unloading represents a time strain which may be totally or partially recoverable with time. Repeated cycles of loading should result in narrower and narrower loops until a straight line relationship is approached.

Figure 13 indicates the increasing shear strength of several different rocks with increasing axial (normal) load (16, 17). This is an important illustration of the increase in rock strength with confinement.

TYPES OF FAILURE

The types of failure with which we are concerned with rocks will be related to either a shearing or a tensile mechanism.

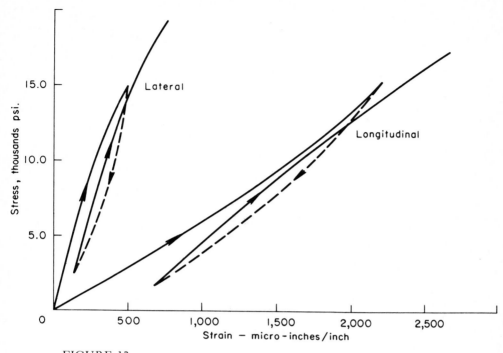

FIGURE 12

Porcupine Dacite

FIGURE 13

Normal Stress and Shear Strength

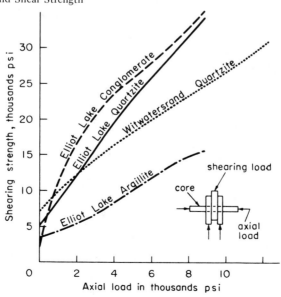

Figure 14 illustrates a typical failure under uniaxial compression. With friction developing restraint on the ends of a test specimen rupture generally is due to conical shear fracture. The inclination of the failure plane is a compromise between the plane of maximum shear and the angle of internal friction of the rock.

Alternatively, if the ends of the specimen are lubricated with paraffin, the splitting failure indicated in figure 15 is characteristic. Here the frictional forces are reorientated and the extruding of the paraffin develops tensile strains. Tensile strains are also developed if the lubricant penetrates any imperfections on the end surfaces. In either case rupture is due to tensile strains.

Specimens under direct tension fail on a plane normal to the direction of the stress with no loss of cross-section. This is the characteristic of brittle fracture. In triaxial compression, sufficient lateral pressure inhibits tensile strain and conical or plane shear failure again takes priority.

THEORIES OF FAILURE

Various theories of failure are developed in "strength of materials" texts which should be referred to at this stage, but, in the practical problem of rock masses, failure is still a qualitative rather than a quantitative phenomenon. Basically, to bridge the gap between theoretical and actual strength, failure theories rest upon Griffith's concept (18) of the propagation of randomly orientated, infinitesimal or incipient cracks. Griffith's theory was modified by McClintock and Walsh (19) to give more realistic results in compression by taking note of the friction between the surfaces of cracks.

Of the various theories of failure, Mohr's perhaps has the widest practical acceptance for rocks. It is based on Coulomb's law of friction which implies failure on any plane when the shearing stress exceeds the combined effect of cohesion and the normal stress on that plane. The development of the failure envelope covering the possible combinations of stress at failure, both tensile and compressive, is dependent on various test results. With this envelope developed failure can be predicted for any combination of principal stresses, the stress circles of which cut the failure envelope (2, 7). Those concerned with rock failure should be familiar with the theory and its graphical presentation.

For a given opening under specific conditions of loading it is possible that the theory of critical strain energy may have an application. This implies failure at some given strain energy content regardless of how it is imposed (5). The condition is illustrated in figure 16 where a low load slowly applied results in more deformation prior to failure than is the case with a higher more rapidly applied load. This places emphasis on time effects and the rate of loading. It also emphasizes the visco-elastic nature of materials such as tar, which shatter under a sudden load (brittle failure) but flow under a steady load.

Other criteria of failure also have been suggested for rocks, but as the critical rock strength may be either tensile or compressive and environmental factors such as those noted below are also involved, the limitations of any single theory are apparent.

FIGURE 14

Failure under Uniaxial
Compression

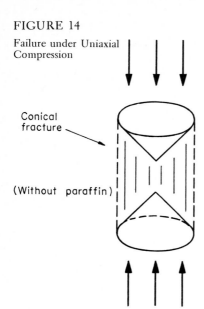

Conical
fracture

(Without paraffin)

FIGURE 15

Splitting Failure
under Uniaxial
Compression

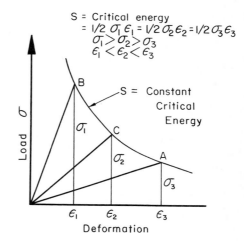

Vertical
tensile
fracture

(With paraffin)

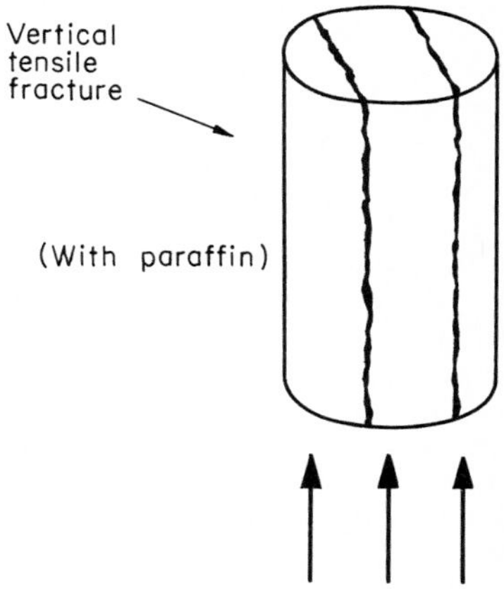

FIGURE 16

Failure Diagram
for Critical
Energy

S = Critical energy
$= 1/2\,\sigma_1\epsilon_1 = 1/2\,\sigma_2\epsilon_2 = 1/2\,\sigma_3\epsilon_3$
$\sigma_1 > \sigma_2 > \sigma_3$
$\epsilon_1 < \epsilon_2 < \epsilon_3$

S = Constant
Critical
Energy

Load σ

Deformation

ENVIRONMENTAL CONDITIONS

These have their effects on rock properties as follows:

Confinement — The loading condition for any mine opening represents some degree of confinement and the degree of confinement influences all strength characteristics as suggested in figure 13. Confinement also adds to the possibility of plastic deformation. However, it is to be noted that in spite of the apparent confinement around mine openings, some conditions of geometry and loading may result in tensile strains on the surface and beyond the opening as shown in figures 28 and 29.

   Solutions — In the extreme case the distinction between clays and rocks derived from them depends upon the moisture content. Usually, for a suite of different rock types, compressive strength and elastic properties vary substantially between water-saturated and oven-dried specimens. The saturated samples are significantly weaker than those of the same type when dried.

   Figure 17 illustrates work by Griggs (20) on specimens of alabaster (massive gypsum–$CaSO_4 \cdot 2H_2O$) surrounded by different solutions. Curve 1 for the dry state

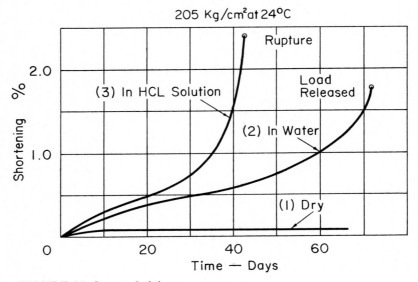

FIGURE 17 Creep of alabaster

indicates that at constant load, deformation reaches a maximum and does not increase further with time. Curve 2 for water-saturated specimens shows deformation proceeding with time under a constant load, and curve 3 shows marked changes in the rate of deformation in a specimen surrounded by an HCl solution. A solution of calcium chloride, in which gypsum is less soluble than in water, also produced a more rapid creep. Thus, solubility alone is not the explanation.

   Orowan (21) points out that molecular cohesion is related to the surface-free energy of a material as follows:

$$\sigma_m = \text{molecular cohesion} = \sqrt{\frac{2\,T\,E}{a}}$$

where   T = surface-free energy

   E = Young's modulus

   a = spacing of atomic planes

As the saturation of a solid by a liquid can lower substantially the surface-free energy of the solid, and thus also the molecular cohesion, it is possible that a reduction in the rupture strength might also follow (22).

In special cases there are other explanations (23) for the effect of solutions on rock properties including ionic mobility and phase changes. A change from solid to fluid in a zone of high pressure and fluid to solid again in the lower pressure area is a possible adjustment to pressure involving recrystallization. Also, the effect of pore water under various conditions of pressure and structure is a consideration for the harder rocks. In the rock mass in the ground water zone there is a weakening influence due to the effect of buoyancy.

Whatever processes may be responsible, the effect of solutions on rock strength is a fact, but the extent to which it could affect practical mining operations is not easy to establish for hard rocks. Generally, except for obvious water-bearing fault lines, Precambrian mine rocks appear dry at very moderate depths if they have not been wetted by water required in the operation.

Temperature — A temperature rise under conditions of differential pressure is generally considered to lower resistance to flow and thus increase mobility. Under very high confining pressure, differential forces at normal temperature have failed to reduce quartz to a plastic state, but quartz appears to be unique in this respect. Geological evidence suggests that in the earth's crust, quartz and other normally brittle rocks behave plastically under certain conditions, of which one would be suitable temperature. In mining, present temperature conditions cannot be an important variable though past conditions may account for some present day strains.

Time — The effect of time on rock failure is an important but not well-understood variable as indicated by day-to-day evidence in most mines. In this respect the writer recalls rock from a shaft bottom at 7500 feet in depth that was still "spitting" on being hoisted to surface, several hours after blasting. Also the caving of excavations through to surface long after mining operations have been discontinued is a common occurrence. Both, no doubt, reflect a slow time strain adjustment in the surrounding rocks. Figure 23 suggests a more positive relationship for certain rock types.

Figures 8 and 9 illustrate time effects on a shale from the United Kingdom. Figures 18 and 19 taken from Griggs' (24) studies represent the effect of time and differential pressure on a specimen of Sölenhofen limestone under a hydrostatic confining pressure of 10,000 atmospheres. Figure 18 shows the deformation for various differential pressures, and the flat portions of the curve indicate flow at constant pressure over a time interval, in the final case proceeding to rupture. Figure 19 shows the nature of the time strain indicated by the horizontal portions of the curves in figure 18 and the variation in the rate of strain is a matter of interest. There is some evidence to suggest that when the rate of strain increases *as in the upper portion of curve 4, figure 19, to cause a reversal of curvature,* rupture will follow ultimately with no additional load.

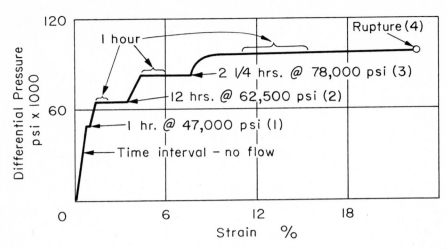

FIGURE 18 The effect of time on the flow of Solenhofen limestone, confining pressure of 10,000 atmospheres

These figures apply to a single rock type (Sölenhofen limestone) under a confining pressure of a somewhat different nature but greatly in excess of that likely to be associated with mining operations. The work illustrates certain important principles, and further studies of a comparable nature on various rock types should contribute to a classification of rocks for mining purposes.

Structural Features — Associated with rock properties, the structural characteristics of the rock mass are likely to be the ultimate variable in determining its reaction to mining operations. When rock properties vary widely between different elements constituting the rock mass, critical stresses will vary likewise. Also, normal stresses can be transmitted directly across a weakness. The proportion of other stresses which can be transmitted will depend upon the normal stress, the cohesion and the frictional resistance of the weakness. Thus, a structurally weakened rock mass, and there are few otherwise within the mining context, can be expected to have local abnormalities in the stress distribution. In the process of rupture, planes of weakness will have first claim on the effects of any concentrations of stress.

Any explanation of the problem of rock failure is dependent on the degree to which any of the above environmental variables dominate a situation. With sudden failure we are dealing with immediately recoverable strain energy and to a lesser extent with the effects of elastic after-working. The presence of any plastic adjustment is a modification limiting the accumulation of strain energy.

An indication of the orders of magnitude of various properties for different rock types is given in table 1 (14). These, in many cases, depend upon testing procedure. Thus, test results relating to the rock substance may be helpful in estimating energy relationships but are of little assistance as failure criteria for a rock mass.

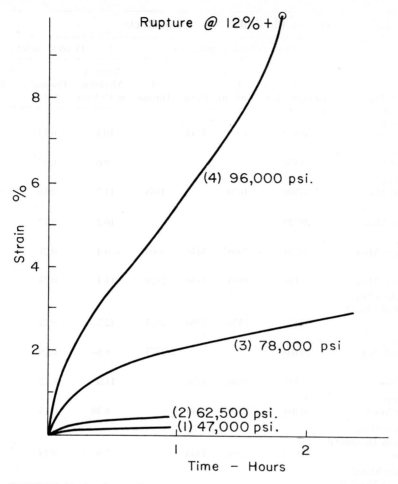

FIGURE 19 Analyses of time strain shown in Figure 18

Subsidence

The stability of unsupported underground excavations is a relative rather than an absolute characteristic. It depends upon a strength-stress relationship which is a function of span and other variables not yet subject to precise calculations. In hard rocks surface subsidence, over apparently self-supporting excavations, has followed long after operations were suspended. In the softer rocks the time factor should be less pronounced.

The relationship between surface subsidence and flat-lying underground excavations has been the subject of continuous study in the coal mining industry where, in spite of varying degrees of predictability and of differences of opinion on the

Table 1 (14) The Physical Properties of Rocks

| Rock Type | STRENGTH (PSI) (UNCONFINED) | | | | ELASTIC MODULI | | |
	a Compression	b Tension	c Shear	d Torsion	Young's Modulus $\times 10^{-6}$ psi	Poisson's Ratio	Modulus of Rigidity $\times 10^{-6}$
Conglomerate, Denison Mine	26890	1090	5745		10.3	0.13	4.5
Quartzite, Denison Mine	23350				9.6	0.17	4.2
Conglomerate, Milliken Mine	17590	1070		1658	13.2	0.10	6.3
Quartzite, Milliken Mine	20720				10.2	0.17	4.3
Porphyry, Lakeshore Mine	36280	1900	3430	3600	9.4	0.21	3.9
Tuff, Lakeshore Mine	38130	1530	3550	2520	11.1	0.23	4.5
Hornblende Schist (Kolar Gold Field, India)	35400	1550	3560	2985	12.7	0.21	5.2
Sandstone, Springhill, N.S.	24160			2375	6.6	0.29	2.6
Porphyry, Sigma Mine	25140	1800	4120		11.0	0.22	
Skarn, Gaspe Copper Mine	30100	1110	3040		8.39	0.15	
Tuff, Helen Mine, Shistoscity Horizontal Banding	31900	2680	3300		7.9	0.14	
Tuff, Helen Mine, Shistoscity Vertical Banding	22500	2510	3200		12.0	0.27	
Norite, Sudbury	27580				9.0	0.17	
Limestone, Trenton (Montreal)	42600				11.2	0.33	
Andesite, Hollinger Mine	12240				7.7	0.17	3.3
Andesite (Red Lake, Ont.)	27500		7890		11.8	0.20	
Rhyolite Breccia (Noranda, Que.)	25780				12.0	0.17	5.1

(a) The uniaxial compression test
(b) The direct-pull tension test
(c) The double shear test
(d) The standard torsion test

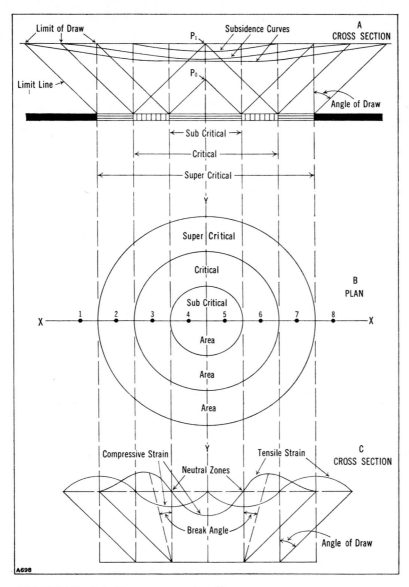

FIGURE 20 Subsidence terminology[25]

mechanics of the process, there is agreement on many aspects of the problem. The National Coal Board in the United Kingdom has summarized the general case, figure 20, and recommended standard terminology (25).

The limiting span of an excavation within which mining can be carried on without surface subsidence is a significant but elusive dimension. It depends upon the accuracy of measurements, but varies with rock types and with depth. In British coal mining practice, for strip-packed longwall panels, subsidence has been related to the width of face/depth of face ratio as shown in figure 21 (26). The curve commences above the zero subsidence line but does suggest for spans of less than one quarter of the depth that subsidence, if any, should be of a very low order. For harder rocks such spans perhaps are greater but an empirical relationship has yet to be established.

Subsidence over underground workings is the result of two opposing factors. The excavation opens up a certain thickness which represents the maximum subsidence possible, but in subsiding the superincumbent rock passes through tension and compression phases which may result in rupture and expanded volume, with the result that even in unsupported areas surface subsidence usually is less than the mined thickness. In hard rocks, at a suitable depth and over limited spans, the expanding volume of the fractured rock can develop sufficient back pressure to regain a comparative stability for the rock mass before any subsidence is apparent at surface. Filling and stowing methods of support only accelerate this trend.

DISPLACEMENTS

In figure 20B (Plan) observation stations are set up along the line X-X. They are levelled and measured precisely with respect to each other before mining commences. Subsequent measurements are then taken as mining progresses. Vertical movement is measured as subsidence, but horizontal movement indicates tensile and compressive strains. If in those cases where the horizontal distance between stations has changed, increases (+) indicating tension are plotted above the mean surface line and decreases (−) indicating compression below this line, we have the strain curves of figure 20C. In general, up to maximum subsidence, compressive strains predominate towards the centre and tensile strains towards the margins of a subsiding area.

THE ANGLE OF DRAW

Figure 20A defines a limit line between the working face and a point on surface beyond which there is no measurable effect as a result of the excavation. The slope of this limit line is referred to as the angle of draw and is measured from the vertical in the United Kingdom and varies with the accuracy of measurement, the amount of subsidence, the width-depth ratio, and with rock properties. With variations in the latter the projection of the limit line at intermediate points may be no more than an approximation to the actual sphere of influence of the excavation.

For British coal measures the angle of draw is perhaps less than 35° but for convenience, and because it holds in some cases (Netherlands), 45° is used in figure 20. For low-dipping deposits not mined through to surface, the subsidence trough is displaced in the dip direction. The angle of draw to the dip side is thus usually greater than to the rise side of an underground excavation but with increasing depth the trend is towards equality. Figure 22 (27) shows for certain British coal measures a relationship between the angle of draw and the width of face / depth of face ratio.

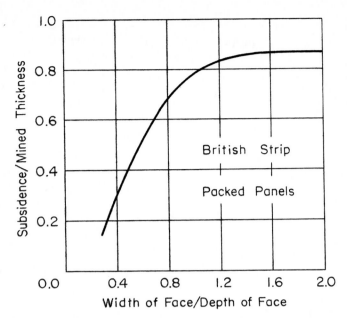

FIGURE 21 (*After R. J. Orchard*[26]) Variations in Subsidence

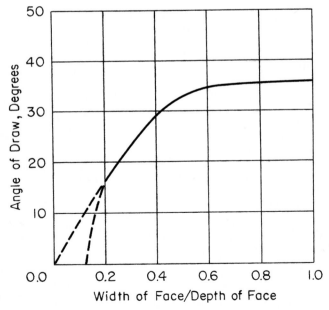

FIGURE 22 (*After J. E. Marr*[27]) Variations in Angle of Draw

THE ANGLE OF BREAK

If now we join the face and the point of maximum tension as shown in figure 20C, this line, within limits, represents the most likely direction of break and the angle which it makes with the vertical is referred to as the angle of break. As rocks trend from plastic to elastic characteristics the angle of draw approaches the angle of break until, with very brittle rocks, they may conform.

THE CRITICAL AREA

Once subsidence over an underground working commences, the area of subsidence will increase as the area of the working increases until a critical area has been worked which results in full subsidence at a point on surface (P_1 in figure 20A). The drawing shows this critical area as being reached when limit lines extended from the faces inwards above the excavation intersect at surface. This rule appears to be an acceptable approximation for coal measure rocks, but may have limitations with harder rocks and steeper limit lines. Further enlargement of the area will proportionately increase the area of full subsidence.

THE TIME FACTOR

The relationship between full subsidence and the thickness of the seam being mined will vary with support, rock types, and with depth, figure 21 (26). Time also has been considered a factor in establishing full subsidence which invariably will be somewhat less than the mined thickness of the seam. However, recent measurements suggest that the time factor in subsidence is more definitely related to depth and rate of face advance than had previously been suspected (28).

Figure 23 represents a section through a seam and a surface point P with the critical area or sphere of influence related to this point indicated by the intersection with the seam of limit lines drawn outwards and downwards from P on each side. The figure is a composite of observations on a number of seams varying somewhat in thickness, inclination, and depth. It shows the average subsidence of comparable points P as a face is advanced over the full critical area. The abscissa is scaled in units of the average radius of the sphere of influence for the seams observed. The ordinate indicates percentages of maximum subsidence. As the seam is mined across the sphere of influence, for each face position the subsidence at P is plotted directly above the face. The curves so obtained and averaged in figure 23 indicate that when the face is directly below P about 15 per cent of the maximum subsidence has taken place. When the face has been extended over the full sphere of influence (2R) about 95 per cent of the maximum subsidence has been recorded. It is only the 5 per cent residual subsidence which is subject to time variations depending on depth and other factors.

Thus, in these rocks for 95 per cent of the subsidence of point P the time factor is dependent on the rate of face advance, depth, and angle of draw, the critical area being dependent on the two latter factors. In the shallower seams the critical area

FIGURE 23 Subsidence and the time factor[28]

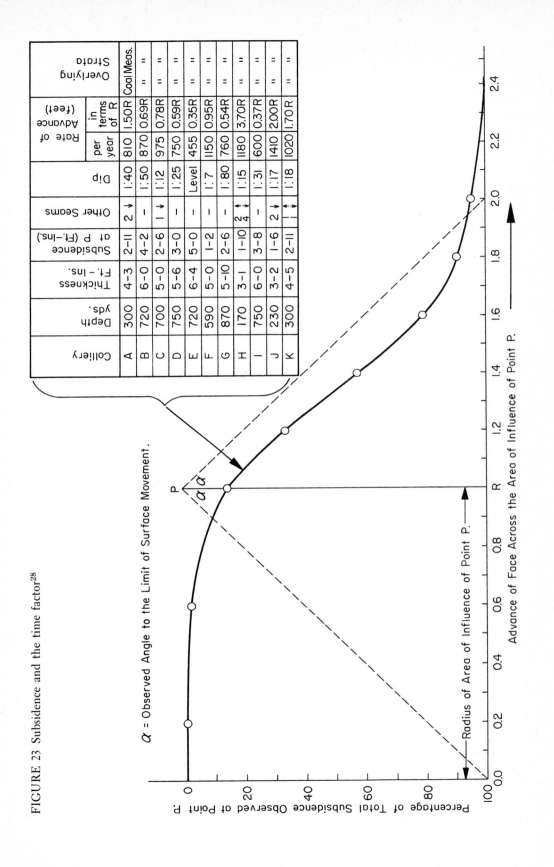

Colliery	Depth yds.	Thickness Ft.-Ins.	Subsidence at P (Ft.-Ins.)	Other Seams	Dip	Rate of Advance per year	in terms of R	Overlying Strata
A	300	4-3	2-11	2 →	1:40	810	1.50R	CoalMeas.
B	720	6-0	4-2	—	1:50	870	0.69R	=
C	700	5-0	2-6	1 →	1:12	975	0.78R	=
D	750	5-6	3-0	—	1:25	750	0.59R	=
E	720	6-4	5-0	—	Level	455	0.35R	=
F	590	5-0	1-2	—	1:7	1150	0.95R	=
G	870	5-10	2-6	—	1:80	760	0.54R	=
H	170	3-1	1-10	←2, 4→	1:15	1180	3.70R	=
I	750	6-0	3-8	—	1:31	600	0.37R	=
J	230	3-2	1-6	2 →	1:17	1410	2.00R	=
K	300	4-5	2-11	←1→	1:18	1020	1.70R	=

α = Observed Angle to the Limit of Surface Movement.

is small, and for a given speed of face advance subsidence is complete much earlier than for deeper workings.

STRAIN

The relationship of strain, subsidence, and depth is indicated from a comparison of different strain profiles, as obtained in figure 20. The strain depends upon the amount of subsidence and the distance over which it is distributed. Generally, the thicker the seam the greater the subsidence and the deeper the seam the greater the distance over which it is distributed. Strain can thus be regarded as directly proportional to the amount of subsidence and inversely proportional to the depth. Thus $E \propto S/h$, where E is the maximum strain, S is the maximum subsidence and h is the depth. Observations in the United Kingdom suggest, as an indication of the order of strain magnitude, that $E = 0.75 \, S/h$ (28).

OPEN PIT OPERATIONS

These represent a special case where freedom from slides depends upon the accuracy of an assumed or calculated angle of draw or break. This angle will vary from the complement of the angle of repose for unconsolidated soils to something approaching the vertical for the most cohesive and hard rock.

A near vertical face, under the strains arising from blasting, depth, temperature changes, moisture, frost, weathering processes, geometry and structure, can be expected to slough off with time. Thus, with few exceptions the over-all slope of open pit walls must anticipate a substantial angle of break, 35°–45° being fairly common. In hard rock open-pit work, the minimum safe angle of break which determines the overall waste to ore ratio is a matter of great economic importance. In the final analysis it is probably most dependent on the natural fracture pattern in the rock mass.

The foregoing sets out the general case for surface subsidence and indicates those points which must be established in order to predict the course of events with accuracy.

Coal mining recognizes no harmless depth beyond which surface subsidence will not appear with time when limiting spans are exceeded. For the harder rocks it is also reasonable to assume, regardless of rock types, depth, and other factors, that if a low-dipping excavation is cut sufficiently thick and extensive laterally, its presence ultimately will be reflected by subsidence at surface.

With steeply dipping hard rock deposits, not mined through to surface, the possibility of significant surface subsidence is more remote. The geometry of the excavation, rock properties, and the pre-mining stress pattern will govern the degree of rock failure, which is usually limited to the vicinity of the excavation. In such cases there is little evidence of angles of draw or limit lines which can be projected for any distance. As alternatives, fracture zones, relaxing zones, and stress zones appear which are no more than initial and localized aspects of the subsidence problem.

Summary and Conclusions

If we knew as much about the properties of the rocks concerned at the beginning of a mining operation as we do at the end, the overall efficiency of many mining operations could be vastly improved. With the science of rock mechanics suitably developed, there is hope that we will not have to await the empirical results available at the end phase to develop the refinement of judgement desired earlier.

Subject to dead weight stability, the response of a rock mass to mining operations is largely dependent upon its elastic, viscous, and plastic properties under the various environmental conditions noted earlier, of which structure claims a top priority. The heterogeneous nature of rocks combined with structural features of rock masses suggests that empiricism will continue to influence judgement as to their behaviour under mining conditions. With the crystalline and metamorphic rocks brittleness limits predictability but with the softer rocks of most coal measures the effects of mining are more positive.

Subsidence represents the vertical component of ground movement related to an excavation. The horizontal components, depending upon whether they are elongations or contractions, represent respectively tensile and compressive strains. Generally, up to full subsidence, compressive strains predominate towards the centre and tensile strains towards the margin of a subsiding area.

The angle of draw varies with the accuracy of measurements, the amount of subsidence, rock properties, and with the width-depth ratio. It defines a limit line beyond which there is no ground movement as a result of an excavation. The angle of break defines the plane of maximum tension. In the United Kingdom both angles are measured from the vertical.

There is no harmless depth beyond which surface subsidence may not appear with time when limiting mining spans are exceeded. However, with depth, other things being equal, surface strains and tilting are moderated.

2 | Stresses and Mine Openings

Sources of Stress in Mines

Stress conditions in the earth's crust must vary substantially from area to area and no doubt locally in any particular area. Probable sources of mining stresses are as follows:

1. A vertical stress due to gravity which is proportional to depth. Elasticity implies a resulting horizontal stress due to Poisson's effect of σ_v/m-1 where σ_v is the vertical stress and m is Poisson's number. A trend from Poisson's effect towards the hydrostatic condition probably follows any transition from brittle to plastic rock properties and the time strains which accompany the latter.

2. Stress changes including time effects, related to the configuration of openings in the rock mass.

3. Stress concentrations and relaxations due to structural conditions locally resulting in bridging or wedging effects within a rock mass.

4. Previous variations in the temperature and loading history of the rocks. Both igneous and sedimentary rocks can carry built-in strains as a result of their mode of formation and subsequent loading history. The latter would include the effects of weathering and glaciation whereby the removal of a substantial depth of rock from above the present surface leaves an uncertain state of strain below, where the horizontal component might well exceed the present gravity load.

5. Tectonic and orogenic processes have been responsible for faulting, shearing and folding, and known variations in surface elevations over geological time. Both earthquakes and gradual changes in relative elevation of different parts of the earth's crust—isostasy—are local confirmation of the existence of such stresses at the present

time. Add to this the current conception of sea floor spreading, and continental drift (29) and stresses in mines in addition to the gravity field should be no cause for surprise.

The first two sources lend themselves to analytical treatment. Stresses due to other sources are sometimes obvious but more often are difficult to differentiate. The overall effect may yield to stress measuring techniques, where strains within the elastic limit only are significant.

The earliest methods were directed towards measuring the difference in strain on a prepared rock surface before and after it is completely relaxed by drilling a continuous slot around it. Suitably orientated measurements, together with an estimate for Young's modulus and Poisson's ratio, permit an estimate of the direction and magnitude of principal stresses. Strains have been measured by tensioned piano wire between points (30), by strain gauges (31, 32), and by photostress plastic (33). However, in all cases variables are present which leave results short of general acceptability.

In other cases, the deformation of a borehole under changing stress conditions has been measured. With this method a small hole is drilled ahead of a rock face, preferably in the direction of one of the principal stresses. A measuring device (34) is then inserted and a reading taken prior to overcoring and relaxing the rock containing the device, when a final measurement is taken. The difference in measurements then indicates the change in diameter due to relaxation. Suitably orientated measurements together with an estimate for Young's modulus and Poisson's ratio also permit an estimate for the direction and magnitude of the principal stresses.

Load cells or stress-meters to read stress changes directly, have been cemented into boreholes. These offer considerable resistance to deformation. They are designed to cover stress changes in the loading of pillars and also absolute stress measurements when the rock containing the cell has been completely relaxed. These cells, many of which require pre-stressing, have the advantage that when working in the range beyond a certain ratio of the modulus of the cell to that of the rock, accuracy in determining the modulus of the rock is not important. Hydraulic (35, 36), magneto-striction (37), and photoelastic principles (33, 38) have been used in the sensing devices of these cells.

Both flat and curved hydraulic jacks (39, 40) also have been used for stress measurements which are not dependent on a knowledge of either Young's modulus or Poisson's ratio. The principle involved for the flat jack is illustrated in figure 24.

Here two or more measuring pins are installed and the distances between them accurately measured. A horizontal slot is then cut centrally as shown and a flat jack is inserted and cemented in the slot. The pressure to which the jack must be raised to restore the original measurements is regarded as an indication of the original stress normal to the slot. Strains also have been measured by strain gauges or strain cells (40). Curved jacks are also used in bore holes with and without overcoring.

The above principles, together with the instruments and the techniques used,

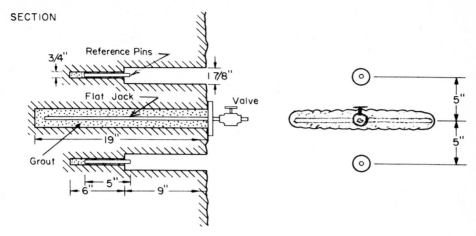

FIGURE 24 Flat Jack Arrangement

are described by Obert and Duvall (3), by E. R. Leeman (32, 41), and by Herget (42, 43). An electrolytic tank has also been used as an analogue for displacements (41, 44, 45).

As a result of the efforts of numerous investigators there is a growing confidence in stress-measuring techniques when the pressure range is well short of failure conditions. Opinions differ, however, as regards the reliability of different methods. They all provide quantitative data but stress changes do affect rock properties (46) suggesting caution in accepting absolute values. We also must bear in mind that other variables may well take priority over the field stress in determining the best mining practice.

In mines the gravity field is always present. By itself, with elastic rock properties, its tensile phases on mine openings represent a limiting condition. Thus designing for greater horizontal stresses, which reduce or eliminate these tensile phases, is justified only when the accuracy of stress measurements is beyond a reasonable doubt.

Stresses around Mine Openings

The analyses of stresses around mine openings have been approached through theoretical mathematics, model studies, and measurements and observations underground.

In the mathematical approach investigations have been based on the theory of elasticity since rheological effects in rocks still await an acceptable mathematical background and rockbursts, in particular, are elastic phenomena. The analytical methods developed in soil mechanics have also been applied. The mathematical approach originally applied to openings, which could be related to mathematical equations; model studies were used for more complicated cases. Later a computerized finite element method was developed (47) that, for both speed and accuracy, has much in its favour.

Model studies have been carried out on photoelastic and photostress models by electrical resistance analogues, on models made from mine rocks, of plaster of Paris, of gels, and more recently of equivalent material with characteristics more similar to those of mine rocks. These latter models are scaled in the most appropriate manner for geometry, load, material strength, and deformation properties and when possible for time.

Methods of applying stress have varied from conventional mechanical and hydraulic methods in uniaxial, biaxial and triaxial tests to the centrifuge principle used in barodynamic tests.

Underground measurements cover a variety of observations. Local conditions of stress and failure have been mapped, the velocity of sound and other elastic characteristics have been measured for different rock types, microseismic activity has been recorded and, as referred to earlier, some success has been attained in measuring the direction and magnitude of stresses in rock in situ.

All these methods combine to give a consistent qualitative picture of stress distribution. However, stress concentrations, tensile or compressive, are quantitatively related to the initial state of stress before an opening is made and, as referred to earlier, techniques for such measurements are still being developed.

In the meantime, as an aid to judgement, the stress distributions associated with spheres and ellipses under different conditions of initial stress are given in the illustrations which follow. The openings are assumed to be in an infinite, isotropic, elastic medium which, amongst other things, implies a depth below surface that is great as compared with the cross-sectional dimensions of the opening. Also, the initial state of stress at the centre of the opening is assumed to be identical with the initial state of stress over the sphere of influence of the opening.

These assumptions associated with the very uncertain properties of rock masses suggest that for the practical problem, absolute stress values must be accepted with caution; their greatest contribution lies in the indication of stress trends.

With the exception of the sphere and spheroids, two-dimensional studies only are involved. This is acceptable for horizontal openings at depth, which are long as compared with their cross-sectional dimensions, when the longitudinal stress is assumed to be uniform for all cross sections. For greater detail, the reader is referred to the work of the U.S. Bureau of Mines (48, 49), H. G. Denkhaus (50), K. Terzaghi and F. E. Richart, Jr. (51), L. Panek (52), and Geldart and Udd (53).

THE SPHERE

In a hydrostatic stress field, which is a limiting condition, the mathematical analysis of the surrounding stress distribution is based on the following formulae by Kirsch in 1898 (54).

$$P_t = -P\left\{\frac{1 + r^3}{2d^3}\right\} \text{ and } P_r = -P\left\{\frac{1 - r^3}{d^3}\right\}$$

where   P = applied stress (Tension +, Compression −)
    P_t = tangential stress
    P_r = radial stress
    r = radius of sphere
    d = distance of any point from centre of sphere or circle
when   d = r (at surface of sphere) P_t max. = 1.5P and P_r = 0

Figure 25 illustrates the distribution—a uniform compression surrounding the sphere—which is a maximum at the boundary, reducing to the applied load at infinity. However, for all practical purposes $P_t = P_r = P$ at one diameter into the surrounding solid rock. Under hydrostatic conditions, with no tensile stress, the sphere shows the lowest maximum compressive stress and thus represents the ultimate stable form.

Figure 26 after Terzaghi and Richart (51) shows the stress distribution vertically upwards above the centre of the sphere and vertically upwards above the ends of the horizontal axis when Poisson's ratio is 0.2. $N = 0.25 = K = \frac{S_x}{S_y}$.

These studies indicate a stress concentration at the surface of the sphere which, with distance from the excavation, gradually approximates the field stress. They also indicate that, as the lateral stress is reduced, the compressive tangential stress at the ends of the horizontal axis increases but over the back, a tensile phase appears for low lateral stress values.

THE CIRCULAR OPENING

This could represent a circular tunnel which is horizontal and long as compared with its cross-sectional dimensions. Here also in a hydrostatic stress field, the stress distribution in the surrounding ground is given by the following formulae, using the notation described for the sphere.

$$P_t = -P\left\{1 + \frac{r^2}{d^2}\right\} \text{ and } P_r = -P\left\{1 - \frac{r^2}{d^2}\right\}$$

Figure 27, also for the hydrostatic condition, shows that the maximum concentration is independent of the size of the circular hole but the depth of abnormal stress surrounding the hole is a function of the radius.

THE GENERAL CASE

The effective outline of any fracture zone related to an underground opening can be only vaguely defined. To develop the general two dimensional case, the assumption that with sufficient pressure it is elliptical in outline, normal to its length, introduces no great error. In this case, assuming free surfaces, figure 28 shows tangen-

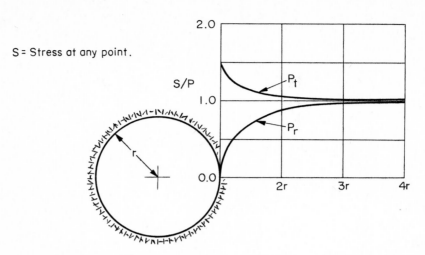

S = Stress at any point.

FIGURE 25 A spheroidal opening in a hydrostatic stress field[54]

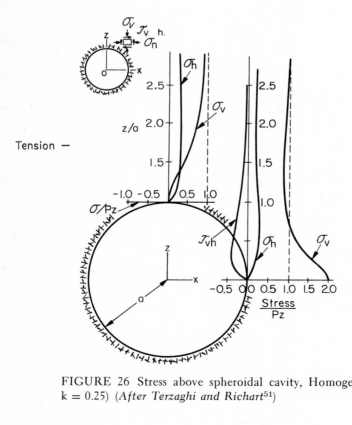

Tension —

FIGURE 26 Stress above spheroidal cavity, Homogeneous Stress Fields (N = k = 0.25) (*After Terzaghi and Richart*[51])

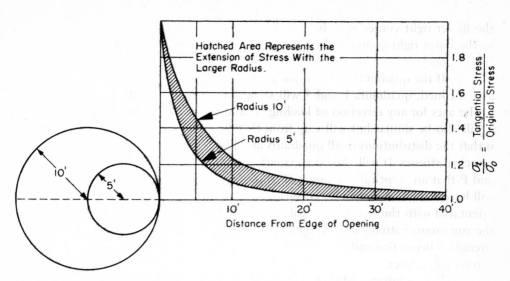

FIGURE 27 Stress Distribution and Size of Opening

tial stresses on elliptical surfaces over a sufficient range of axis and stress ratios and inclinations to establish trends.

The sub-figures vary, left to right, towards increasing axis ratios and from the top down towards increasing stress ratios. Upwards towards k = 0 (unidirectional) and to the right towards v = infinity (a crack), the variation in each case is towards increasing maximum and decreasing minimum stresses, the latter ranging to tension for low stress ratios and high axis ratios. The analyses, by Geldart and Udd, (53) are derived from the following formula.

$$\frac{\sigma_\eta}{S_y} = \frac{2v\,(1 + k) + (1 - k)\,(1 - v^2)\,\cos 2\beta + (1 - k)\,(1 + v)^2\,\cos 2(\beta - \eta)}{(1 + v^2) + (1 - v^2)\,\cos 2\eta}$$

where σ_η = tangential stress on the elliptical surface
v = semi-major axis / semi-minor axis = axis ratio
k = S_x / S_y = pre-mining horizontal / vertical stress = stress ratio
β = angle clockwise from semi-major axis to S_x
η = elliptical co-ordinate measured clockwise from the semi-major axis

Figure 28 is based on elastic theory and assumes, regardless of the state of stress, that material always is within the elastic limit. In practice this assumption is limited by the strength properties of a rock mass and critical stresses may be either tensile or compressive. With both tensile and compressive stresses on a free surface, with varying stress and axis ratios, one or the other eventually must exceed the elastic limit for any rock type.

The steepness of the stress gradient between maximum tension and maximum compression for inclined openings under the conditions represented towards

the upper right corner is to be noted. If a diagonal is drawn from the upper left to the lower right corner of figure 28, tensile stress conditions in general are above the diagonal.

If the quadrants of an ellipse are numbered as in figure 28H, then, with the axes inclined, quadrants 1 and 3 will show similar stress distributions with respect to the axes for any direction of loading. The stress distributions of quadrants 2 and 4 will also be similar but will vary from that for quadrants 1 and 3. The exception is that the distributions in all quadrants are similar when the axes are parallel to the principal stresses. It will also be apparent, for $\beta = 90°$, in figure 28, sub-figures H, L, and P that an elliptical opening with the axis ratio the reciprocal of the stress ratio will have a uniform stress concentration around its periphery when the major axis is orientated with the major principal stress. Such an opening would be stable within the compressive strength range for a reasonably homogeneous rock type. If the rock strength is below this uniform value an opening cannot be self-supporting. This aspect is referred to later.

For an interpretation of the graphs of figure 28 consider sub-figure H. Here $k = 1/3$ and $v = 3$. For $\beta = 0°$, at the end of the major axis, $\eta = 0°$, the tangential stress is about 6.7 times S_y, falling to zero at $\eta = 50°$, to a tension of $-0.4\,S_y$ at $\eta = 90°$, to zero again at $\eta = 130°$ and to 6.7 S_y at the other end of the major axis at $\eta = 180°$. It will be noted again that, for $\beta = 90°$, a uniform stress exists around the surface of the ellipse.

Stresses on the surface of an opening are a reflection of those in depth around the opening. The latter have been calculated for elliptical openings by Mahtab (55) and for ovaloidal openings by Dhar (56); a summary of both has been prepared by Dhar, Geldart, and Udd (57).

St. Venant's principle recognizes significant stress changes as a result of an opening for depths around the opening of two to three times the maximum cross-sectional dimension. Figure 29 suggests that for all practical purposes, the major stress changes occur within one major cross-sectional dimension around the opening. Thus, when two openings are separated by a distance greater than the sum of their maximum cross-sectional dimensions, the stress changes around either opening, due to the proximity of the other, will be very small. Inhomogeneities and structural irregularities can vary the effect and, in practice, a factor of safety for such contingencies may be desirable, areas of both compression and of tension being considered.

Given the free development of these stress patterns with depth, as stoping spans are extended tangential tensile failure will develop in the walls or shear failure must develop at the face. Add to this gravitational body forces creating a vertical tension in the hangingwall and compression in the footwall, and a reason for stresses in excess of rock strength is apparent.

The application of these graphs, figures 28 and 29, to the practical problem can be further illustrated by a consideration of the following (two-dimensional) analyses (i) stresses induced by block caving and (ii) stresses induced by shrinkage stoping.

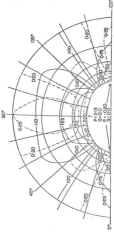

—Contours of major principal stresses (solid lines) and minor principal stresses (broken lines) around an elliptical opening for which V = 1.5, k = 0.2, β = 0 degrees.

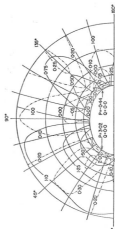

—Contour of major principal stresses (solid lines) and minor principal stresses (broken lines) around an elliptical opening for which V = 1.5, k = 0.2, β = 90 degrees.

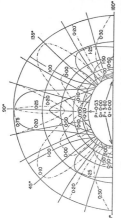

—Conventions Used for Ellipses

where:—

ξ, η   elliptical co-ordinates

ξ₀   co-ordinate corresponding to the boundary of the hole

β   angle between major axis and Sx (measured clockwise from major axis)

Sx, Sy   orthogonal applied stresses along X and Y axes

$S_x/S_y = k$ = the applied stress parallel to the "X" and "Y" axes.

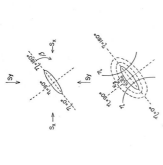

—Contour of major principal stresses (solid lines) and minor principal stresses (broken lines) around an elliptical opening for which V = 1.5, k = 0.2, β = 45 degrees.

FIGURE 29 Stresses in depth around elliptical openings under varying loads and inclinations. (*After Mahtab*[55])

Stresses Induced by Block Caving (58) — As most mine openings can be generalized into an elliptical outline, given estimates for the stress ratio and the inclination of the principal stresses, the trend in stress concentrations as the axis ratio is extended can be readily approximated for any axis inclination.

Recent articles on block caving have inspired the author to examine that operation within the above context. This involves estimating, from the graphs, the progressive stress changes induced as caving develops above the undercut of an area laid out for block caving. The stresses above the undercut of a block 200 feet × 200 feet and 400 feet high, reaching to surface, under two different conditions of loading, are considered in figures 30A and 30B.

Two-dimensional analyses for the stresses around mine openings, as referred to in figure 30, assume an infinite, isotropic, elastic medium and also that openings are long with respect to their cross-sectional dimensions. In the comparisons which follow, liberties are taken with each assumption. The operation, within 400 feet of the surface, compromises the infinite medium concept, and the undercut is square, not long, with respect to cross-sectional dimensions. These variations throw a shadow over absolute values, but should not upset the generality of the stress trends. This also holds for the fact that caving is largely confined to the upper part of the ellipse. However, a fracture zone may develop below the undercut.

In figure 30A the field stress is the gravity load. This, based on a depth of 400 feet, is of the order of 480 psi in the vertical direction. With a Poisson's ratio for the rock of 0.25, the horizontal stress would approach 160 psi to give a stress ratio or k factor of 160/480 or 1/3 at the undercut. A lower Poisson's ratio gives a lower k factor which results in greater maximum stresses in both tension and compression for any caving outline as well as more favourable caving conditions.

Different outlines in the progress of caving are numbered 1 to 4 and expressed in terms of their axes ratios. For an undercut 200 feet square × 10 feet high, in cross-section, the axis ratio v approximates 200/10 or 20 and similarly for the other outlines noted. The stress distributions scaled below the undercut, in the case of figure 30A, are in units of the vertical load; one unit = 480 psi. In both figures 30A and 30B compression is positive (+) and tension is negative (−).

In figure 30A, on completion of the undercut, a horizontal tension of about 0.7 units or 0.7 × 480 = 336 psi would exist over much of the back. This probably exceeds the tensile strength of the rock mass and the effect would be to open joint planes to the degree where dead weight would induce local and progressive caving. At the surface of the abutments there would be a vertical compression of about 20,000 psi. This might induce shearing to increase the radius of curvature at the abutments and also facilitate the caving process.

If caving should progress through the different outlines shown, which grow progressively less favourable, the stress distribution is a curve, convex downwards, indicating tangential tension gradually giving way to compression over the back. At outline no. 4, v = 3, *with the major axis vertical,* there is a uniform tangential compression of 1.3 × 480, or about 624 psi, over the whole surface of the section. This

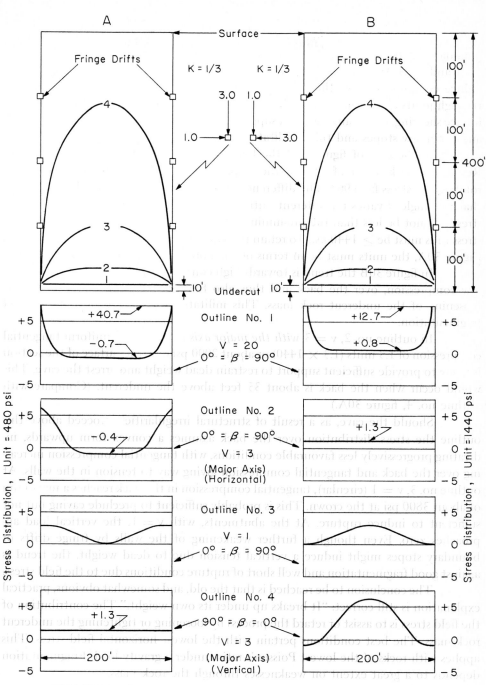

FIGURE 30 Caving outlines and stress distributions

represents a condition of restraint which, in resisting dead weight, might arrest the cave. However, the weakening effects of abutment shearing, fringe drifts and / or boundary stopes are likely to be such that the natural caving outline will vary between no. 1 and no. 3. Within this range the effect of the field stress is to induce tension or reduce compression over the back and give dead weight every chance to operate through joints and weaknesses in the rock mass. Compression at the abutments may induce shearing, but in any case, will supplement the weakening effects of fringe drifts and boundary stopes and thus facilitate caving.

In the case of figure 30B the horizontal stress is three times the vertical. Retaining the k factor of 1/3 for the graphs, this condition may be obtained by rotating the stress field 90°. The difference between figures 30A and 30B thus is only that the angle β varies for different outlines as noted in the drawings. The vertical stress will not be less than the pre-mining gravity load of 480 psi and the horizontal stress thus must be $\geq$ 1440 psi. To retain the same divisions of stress distribution as in Figure 30A, the units must be in terms of the horizontal load — 1 unit = 1440 psi.

In figure 30B the trend is towards high compression, rather than tension and low compression, over the back and thus also towards a tightening rather than a loosening of the undercut rock mass. This militates against free caving and good fragmentation.

In outline no. 2, v = 3 *with the major axis horizontal,* a uniform tangential compression of 1.3 units (1.3 $\times$ 1440) or about 2000 psi over the surface of the section is likely to provide sufficient support to restrain dead weight and arrest the cave. This would occur when the back is about 35 feet above the undercut. (Compare with outline no. 4, figure 30A.)

Should the cave, as a result of structural irregularities, proceed above this outline the stress distribution over the back assumes a convex form upwards, indicating progressively less favourable conditions, with tangential compression increasing over the back and tangential compression giving way to tension in the walls. At outline no. 3, v = 1 (circular), tangential compression in the back reaches a maximum of about 3800 psi at the crown. This is probably sufficient to preclude caving but not sufficient to induce rupture. At the abutments, with v = 1, the vertical load approaches zero. Even though a further weakening of the walls by fringe drifts or boundary stopes might induce a vertical tension due to dead weight, the trend is against good fragmentation and well short of rupture conditions due to the field stress.

The conclusion to be reached is that the old, and somewhat obvious, practical explanation is still correct: "It breaks up under its own weight." The contribution of the field stress is to assist or retard the process by loosening or tightening the undercut rock mass. The best conditions pertain with the lowest horizontal field stress. This applies with rocks of the lowest Poisson's ratio, under a gravity load. Fragmentation depends to a great extent on weaknesses through the rock mass.

Stresses Induced by Shrinkage Stoping (59) — The stress pattern around shrinkage stopes is identical with that around other stopes under the same physical conditions. However, a shrinkage stope ends as an unsupported open stope and the method is limited to the stress range within which the rock is generally self-supporting.

Again, generalizing the stope outline into an elliptical cross-section provides a good base for approximating the stress distribution as mining progresses. However, with failure conditions in the walls, the axis ratio as cut gives way to an effective axis ratio in which the apparent minor axis, as reflected in the curvature of failure at the face, is greater than the as-cut dimension. This places a question mark over absolute values, but again, should not upset the generality of stress trends.

For present purposes, a long flat back stope 7 feet wide, inclined 60° to the horizontal, at a depth of 1500 feet is considered. This gives a vertical pre-mining stress, due to gravity only, of about 1500×1.2, or 1800 psi. With a Poisson's ratio of 0.25 the stress ratio or k factor is 1/3 to give a horizontal field stress of 600 psi. A lower Poisson's ratio, inducing higher maximums in both tension and compression, invites earlier failure. The stope is set out in cross-section in figure 31.

The tangential stress distributions at the surface of the opening, compression $(+)$ and tension $(-)$, also shown in figure 31 are taken from figure 28 for the relevant axis ratios and stress ratios for the ellipse inclined at 60°. These distributions are most useful in a qualitative sense for the purpose of indicating trends. However, with caution the units shown may be multiplied by the vertical stress of 1800 psi to indicate orders of magnitude. If the unconfined rock strength is taken as 1200 psi in tension and 4000 psi in shear, disregarding weaknesses, critical values will be apparent in the stress distributions.

The hangingwall stress distribution is best illustrated by fitting the stope section of the graph (figure 31) to its counterpart in the stoping cross-section with the right side of the graph upward and to the right. At this stage the study is simplified if stresses are assumed to be within the elastic limit of the rock.

On this basis, commencing with the back taken down at v = 3, a tangential compression, well in excess of the field stress, is apparent in the vicinity of both face and floor. Also on the hangingwall, below the face, there is an area where the stress approaches zero. As the stope is carried upwards, extending the axis ratio, compression increases in the vicinity of the face and floor and the zero stress area, below the face, gives way to tangential tension over an increased range. The maximum tensile value also increases with the axis ratio. The tensile phase follows the upward progress of the face and thus, beyond v = 3, traverses all newly exposed hangingwall with a gradually increasing intensity. As it advances it is replaced by recompression below.

Tension in the hangingwall permits dead weight to operate and at any stage the displacement of a block opens the way for others to follow. Thus long before the stope reaches the floor pillar above, waste may be mixed with the ore. When stresses exceed the tensile strength of the rock, or even of its jointing system, the upper hangingwall is in a loosened condition. Withdrawing the support of the broken ore in the final pulling of the stope, leaves an over-hanging wall with its capacity for self-support thus largely eliminated. Portions of it naturally fall in and mix with the ore until all the loosened mass is involved.

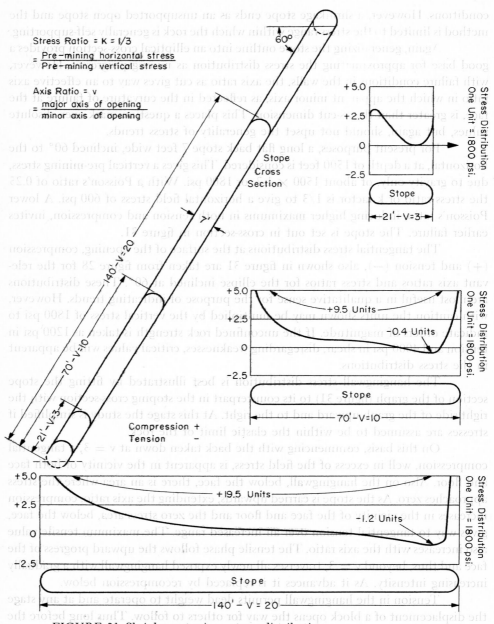

FIGURE 31 Shrinkage stoping—stress distribution

In the footwall the stress distribution is approximated by fitting the stope section of the graph (figure 31) to its counterpart in the stoping cross-section so that the graph is inverted to the footwall with its right side now downwards and to the left. At any stage the stress distribution is thus the reverse of that in the hangingwall, high compression at the face and floor but with the lower part of the footwall in tension. However, except for some increase in length as the stope extends upwards, the tensile zone is static and does not traverse the footwall as it does the hangingwall. The upper part of the footwall is thus always in compression. However, the maximum tensile value in the lower part increases with the axis ratio and approximates that in the upper hangingwall unless failure intervenes.

With rocks of limited strength in tension and shear the practical implications of these stress changes are obvious. With both tensile and shearing strains progressively increasing, at some stage failure of one or both types must follow. Shear failure would be most conspicuous in the vicinity of the face and floor and tensile failure in the upper hangingwall and lower footwall. Failure of either type lowers an effective axis ratio and thus reduces maximum stresses in both tension and compression. However, once failure sets in, the gradual nature of the process requires that one or other of these stresses be maintained at the point of incipient failure.

The fact that the lower part of the footwall is also loosened by tensile strains is perhaps less serious, but even here, if a block is displaced during chute pulling others are likely to follow.

Practice has clearly established the ground problem associated with shrinkage stoping. The foregoing does no more than offer an explanation based on the controlling variables, axis ratio, stress ratio, and rock strength. Dilution is simply the expression of rock failure due to the operation of one or more of these variables. Shortened spans, rock bolting, and other forms of support are palliatives which may buy time but will not arrest the trend. Dilution means the loss of self-supporting capacity upon which shrinkage stoping depends and with its development the competitive advantage of the method rapidly recedes.

Corners — The stress concentration associated with sharp corners is another important consideration in mine design. Theoretically at sharp corners with no radius of curvature the compressive stress increases without limit. In mine excavations, even at shallow depth some curvature is necessarily always present. At depth, arching of excavations may commence due to shearing as a result of high corner stresses. Approximate distributions with some radius of curvature, after the U.S. Bureau of Mines, (48) are shown in figures 32 and 33. See also reference 49.

Multiple Openings and Pillars — When an excavation is enlarged towards another excavation and the intervening ground is reduced to less than the sum of the largest cross-sectional dimension normal to the length of each excavation, the stress concentration of one excavation is gradually superimposed upon the sphere of in-

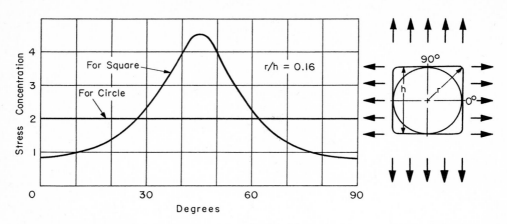

FIGURE 32 Stress distribution around a square opening with rounded corners in a hydrostatic stress field[48]

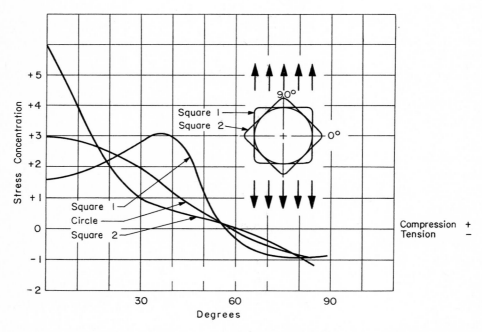

FIGURE 33 Stress distribution on the boundary for three different shaped openings. Unidirectional stress field[48] (See also reference 49)

fluence of the other. From this point, for the purpose of analysis, the intervening ground becomes a pillar with the stress concentrations associated with such structures. In stoping areas, rib and crown pillars isolated on two or three sides, projections forming acute angles and ground isolated on four sides all take on pillar loading characteristics.

It will be noted that while ground gradually reduced to pillar dimensions results in stress, and thus energy concentrations, if the pillar is cut out originally to a small size, as in the case of thin rib pillars, its failure can follow gradually with mining. Such pillars usually have some supporting value after failure but there is little build-up of strain energy as a result of their use. Many rib pillars are developed in this manner, designed for gradual failure.

Theoretically, pillar loading should represent some combination of stresses generated by the individual openings forming the pillar. The stress contours after Udd and Nair (60) for the major and minor principal stresses P and Q respectively, in the ground constituting a pillar structure are shown in figures 34 to 39 for ovaloids of different inclinations, and other parameters as stated. They show the characteristic concentration of the P stresses and tensile values in the Q stress range. The maximum shear stress, $\dfrac{P - Q}{2}$, reaches high values for inclined openings. The U.S. Bureau of Mines (48) has shown that with increasing extraction the average shear stress in pillars increases more rapidly than the maximum until at very high extractions the average approximates the maximum.

Figure 40, also the result of studies by the U.S. Bureau of Mines (48), indicates for vertical loading an increasing maximum stress with increasing ratios of opening width to pillar width, and with the number of pillars. Figure 41, also with vertical loading, relates the maximum stress concentration to the number of pillar lines established (48). Figure 42 indicates the more rapid increase in pillar stress, associated with high extraction (48), when the full superincumbent load is carried by the pillars.

It is sufficient at this stage to record that pillars are compressive stress raisers of a high order with tension also appearing for some conditions of geometry and loading. These aspects require consideration in problems of mine design. The subject of pillar loading and pillar strength will be discussed in greater detail under "support."

The Range of Stress Changes

Stress conditions in an operating mine are seldom static. The strength-stress ratio at any point changes with every blast. With depth and with increasing mined area the trend is towards deteriorating ground conditions. This trend is reflected in the sloughing of development openings, through failure in tension or shear, to shapes which are more stable under the conditions existing. An indication of the direction in

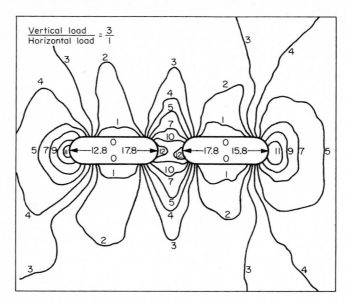

FIGURE 34 Stress contours, major principal stress (P) in multiples of the vertical load[60]

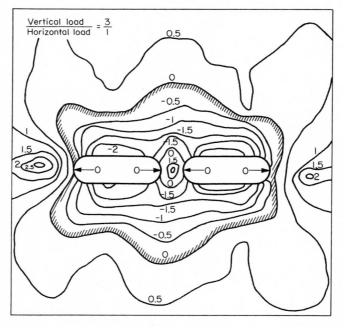

FIGURE 35 Stress contours, minor principal stress (Q) in multiples of the vertical load[60]

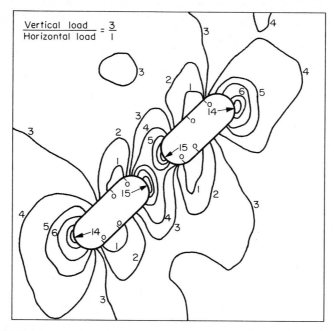

FIGURE 36 Stress contours, major principal stress (P) in multiples of the vertical load[60]

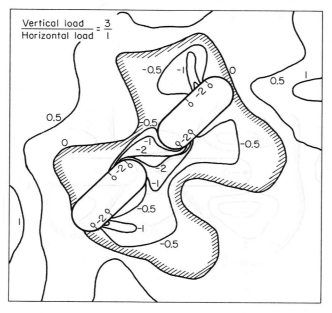

FIGURE 37 Stress contours, minor principal stress (Q) in multiples of the vertical load[60]

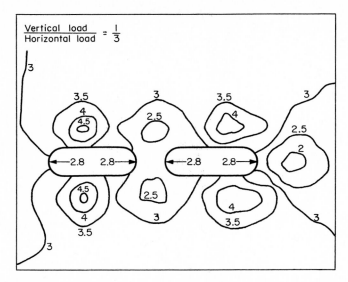

FIGURE 38 Stress contours, major principal stress (P) in multiples of the horizontal load[60]

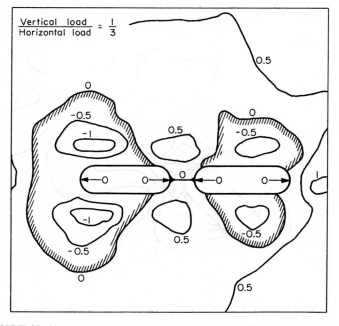

FIGURE 39 Stress contours, minor principal stress (Q) in multiples of the horizontal load[60]

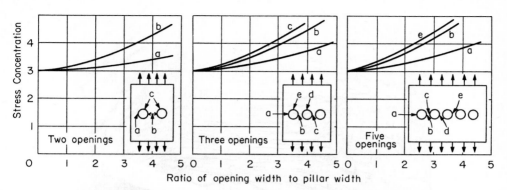

FIGURE 40 Stress concentration as a function of the number of pillars and the ratio of opening width to pillar width in an applied stress field

FIGURE 41 Pillar Loading and Pillar Lines

FIGURE 42 Pillar Loading and Extraction

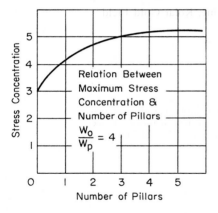

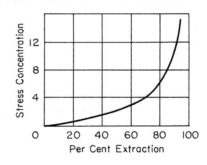

Figures 40, 41 and 42 after Duvall[48]

which an opening has been driven is sometimes apparent from the direction of the remnants of such failure planes, figures 43 and 44. The same holds for an advancing stope face, figure 45, where with increasing span, stress adjustment suggests failure at the face on an increasing radius of curvature, figure 46, but this still requires confirmation.

Narrow tabular orebodies are frequently associated with wall rocks having planes of weakness, such as schistosity or bedding, paralleling the orebodies. As open stoping spans are extended in such orebodies, an early indication of ground pressure is the sagging of the hangingwall and later a heaving of the footwall due, in part, to decompression and to dead weight failure along these planes.

Shrinkage stoping also gives good illustrations of the onset of failure in the walls of an excavation. With self-supporting ground this method is in its natural

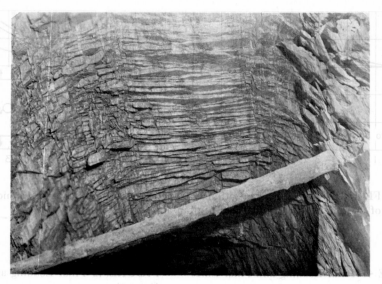

FIGURE 43   48th level Nundydroog Mine, Kolar Gold Field

NOTE: In figures 43, 44 and 45 there is some doubt as to the relative
place of tension and shear in the mechanism involved; see
references 61, 62, 63 and 64, also figures 28, 29 and 54.

Drift Face—Longitudinal Sections—Stope Face

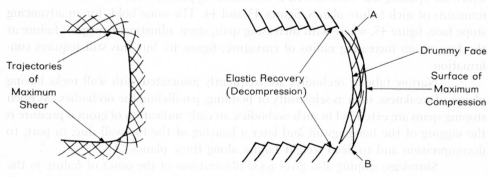

FIGURE 45 Stresses on Drift and Stope Faces

FIGURE 44 Excavating a sump below a crosscut, in granite, on the 950 level of the Director Mine, St. Lawrence, Newfoundland. The "free shear" cracks below the floor, certainly related to tectonic strain, are similar to those in the back in figure 43. (*Photo by A. B. Dory, Courtesy of The Aluminum Company of Canada, Limited.*)

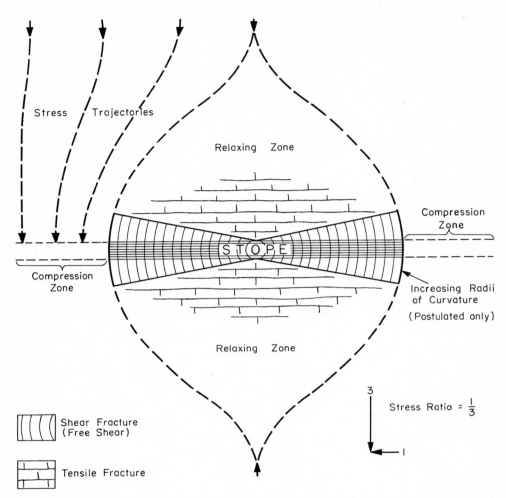

Stress Trajectories

Relaxing Zone

Compression Zone

Compression Zone

Relaxing Zone

Increasing Radii of Curvature (Postulated only)

STOPE

Shear Fracture (Free Shear)

Tensile Fracture

3

Stress Ratio = $\frac{1}{3}$

1

FIGURE 46 Hypothetical conditions surrounding a horizontal excavation at depth (low stress ratios)

element, but practice shows that at some moderate depth, in any mine a stage is reached where the walls lose their self-supporting ability (see figure 31) and the final pulling of stopes is accompanied by excessive dilution. At this stage, the boundary of a stope when pulled empty may bear little relationship to the original excavation.

It has long been recognized that when ground failure becomes a factor, shrinkage stoping gives way to other methods, grade permitting. These are usually cut and fill, which exert some control over wall movements. At depth, even with the best filling practice, wall closure is apparent in filled stopes and in levels through filled areas. Suitably located openings in the walls of both open and filled stoping areas suggest displacements if not fractures to depths which appear to bear some relation to the span, figure 55.

Obviously the creation of an excavation in ground under pressure is followed by a substantial stress adjustment in the surrounding rock in reaching towards a new condition of equilibrium. In theory, stress changes as a result of an opening extend for an infinite distance. In practice they are significant for a limited multiple of the maximum cross-sectional dimension of the opening normal to its length. The pre-mining stress field is an unavoidable fact and in ground control we are interested primarily in conditions which increase or decrease original strains.

Stress changes on the surface of single openings for various loadings are shown in figure 28 and in depth around such openings, over a limited range of conditions, in figure 29. Stress distributions associated with pillars are also shown for some conditions in figures 34 to 39.

It may be noted that from any point on the boundary of an opening or its fracture zone deep enough to exclude significant ground surface effects, all outward directions lead to approximately pre-mining strains. Under many conditions of loading there is a range over which these directions conform with stress gradients showing compressive strains in excess of pre-mining values. Over a more restricted range there is a transition from relaxation, including tension, to pre-mining strain values without significantly greater strains in the progression, figure 29.

With the pre-mining condition of strain as the standard, stress changes thus can be roughly segregated into a compression zone where strains are equal to or greater than pre-mining values and a relaxing zone where strains are less. In the latter zone, on a bulk or volumetric basis, tensile strain is an amplification of compressive strain recovery. When elastic limits are exceeded, in either tension or compression, rupture follows to initiate a fracture zone. These three zones are interdependent and arise with the shift in stress trajectories necessary to by-pass an opening, figures 46 and 52. They thus cover the range of significant stress changes related to the opening.

THE COMPRESSION ZONE

This zone of converging stress trajectories, if not significantly within the sphere of influence of other openings, soon becomes stabilized with or without failure in the related opening. However, unless provided for in the layout, such static conditions are very temporary in an operating mine.

Stoping is the most active cause of stress changes and, in the stoping plane, carries on its periphery a compression zone which follows the advance of the working face. Thus, stope faces passing over an opening in the hangingwall or footwall superimpose the stoping compression zone on that of the opening and failure on the surface of the opening may follow. Numerous cases are on record where failure in openings within the walls has been predictably associated with the advance of stope faces. These effects, following the face, give way to a relaxing zone which follows the compression zone.

Pillar loading is a superimposing of stress zones and it is useful to recall figure 42 which indicates that with increasing extraction in a pillar-supported area, the pillar stress values trend towards infinity. Thus failure will intervene at some stage in the loading process.

Compression zones associated with single openings cannot be avoided, but good design if not based on pillar support will ensure that pillar-loading characteristics are reduced to a minimum at every stage in the progress of mining.

A further concentration of stress follows when the sphere of influence of the compression zone reaches towards faults, dykes, and similar discontinuities. The closer the direction of stope faces approaches the normal to the strike of such structures the better ground conditions are likely to be.

The increased strain in a compression zone represents a contraction of the rock mass involved, at the expense of excavated volume. This reduction in volume, to the degree that elastic theory applies, must be transferred within the elastic limit to surface as subsidence of a very low order. This is shown on an exaggerated scale in figure 53.

One of the earliest types of failure to be observed is a sloughing of thin plates of rock sheared roughly parallel to a free face. With sufficient pressure the shearing will follow the curvature of a face regardless of its direction. The explanation usually advanced is that shear failure at $45° + \emptyset/2$ ($\emptyset$ is the angle of internal friction) to a free face, releases an area which can then also decompress laterally, parallel to the outline of the opening. This lateral expansion operating against the restraint of the rock constituting the surface of maximum compression results in a pinching effect with little or no normal stress, thus freeing an area parallel to the face which peels off as a thin plate. Such plates are shown in figures 47 and 48. (Photographs by Dr. D. F. Coates.)

This is a universal type of failure characteristic of compression zones when ground pressure exceeds the unconfined shearing strength of rocks. For lack of a better expression it will be referred to as a "free-shear." The mechanism probably varies only in degree from that in the discing of drill core (61, 62, 63, 64), in the laminated failure of figures 43 and 44, and perhaps also in the Brazilian (tensile) test.

Griffiths (18) has suggested that the maximum stress on the surface of elliptical openings will vary with the ratio c/r, where c is the semi-span and r is the radius of curvature of the face, small compared with c (refer to figures 43, 44, 49, 50 and 51 for actual conditions).

Stope faces at depth, and particularly longwall faces, are usually advanced under a state of incipient failure. The face is drummy, suggesting that the fracture zone extends for some distance beyond. Incipient failure at the face implies a failure value which is the resultant of "free-shear" forces and those normal to the interface between compression and fracture zones. This also implies a fairly constant c/r ratio, r increasing with c, if the mining width is constant.

In figure 28 it will be seen that, with variation in the stress ratio, the axis ratio and the inclination of the opening with respect to the stress axis, the tangential stress at points A and B, figure 45, can be varied between high compression and high tension. Fractures arising as a result ("free-shear" or tensile) parallel to the original

FIGURE 47 Free shear specimens of Elliot Lake quatzites and conglomerates

FIGURE 48 Free shear specimens of greenstones and concrete (light colour)

FIGURE 49 Stanrock Mine, Elliot Lake, Ontario. Note curved side wall of service-way[68]

stope face, can extend for many feet into the hangingwall and footwall. Figure 54 confirms tensile possibilities.

THE RELAXING ZONE

The compression zone, limited to stress conditions maintaining or increasing pre-mining strains, implies a compensating relaxing zone where stress trajectories diverge to provide varying degrees of de-stressing, extending through tensile strains to rupture. For a given axis ratio these tensile stresses increase with decreasing stress ratios. Thus, for gravity loading, rocks with the lowest Poisson's ratio will induce the highest tensile stress.

The relaxing zone, in general, occurs within the compression zone, as shown in figures 46 and 52. The extension into the walls of both zones depends upon the span of the opening.

The effect of span is well illustrated in the classical experiment carried out in the ventilation shaft of the Harmony Gold Mine in South Africa, (41, 65, 66). This shaft, vertical, circular, and concrete-lined to a diameter of 24 feet, intersects the reef, dipping at 7° at a vertical depth of 4365 feet. Measuring points were installed in the shaft and checked periodically as stoping was extended outwards from the shaft bottom to give the displacements indicated in figure 55. The measurements also show the proportion of wall closure ascribed to the heaving of the footwall.

FIGURE 50 Lac-
nor Mine, Elliot
Lake, showing a
pillar face form-
ing the curved side
wall of a stope[68]

FIGURE 51 Stan-
leigh Mine, Elliot
Lake, shearing of
back adjacent to a
crushed pillar[68]

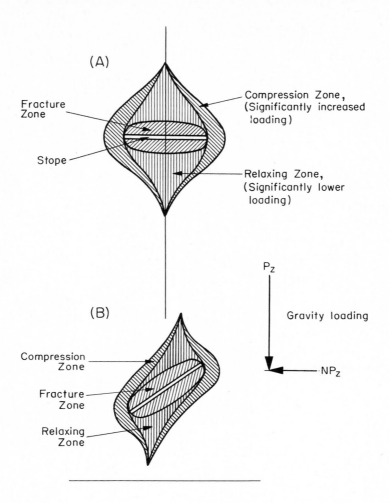

(A)

Fracture
Zone

Compression Zone,
(Significantly increased
loading)

Stope

Relaxing Zone,
(Significantly lower
loading)

P_z

Gravity loading

(B)

Compression
Zone

Fracture
Zone

Relaxing
Zone

NP_z

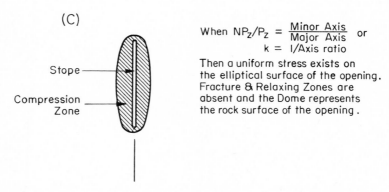

(C)

Stope

Compression
Zone

When $NP_z/P_z = \dfrac{\text{Minor Axis}}{\text{Major Axis}}$ or
$k = 1/\text{Axis ratio}$

Then a uniform stress exists on
the elliptical surface of the opening.
Fracture & Relaxing Zones are
absent and the Dome represents
the rock surface of the opening.

FIGURE 52 Compression, Relaxing and Fracture Zones (Generalized)

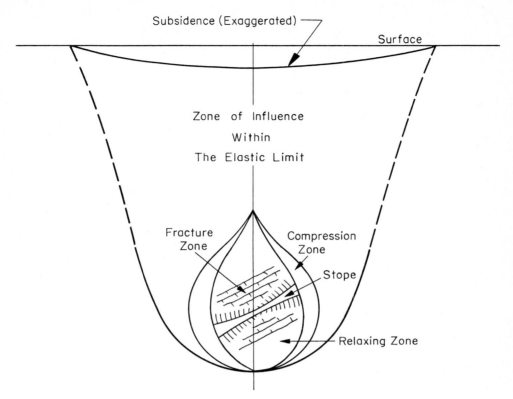

FIGURE 53 Elastic Adjustment at Surface for a Mine Excavation

Emphasizing the exponential relationship between span (area) and volume, it will be apparent that a marginal increase in the greater span involves stress changes in a much larger volume of rock than would be the case for a shorter span. This exponential factor with an increasing axis ratio offers an explanation for the fact that stoping areas with large spans are frequently troubled with pressure problems not so obvious with shorter spans at similar depth.

Failure in the relaxing zone may be of tensile origin but figures 28 and 29 suggest that tension occurs in a limited range only, over the lower stress and higher axis ratios. However, deadweight body forces contributing to failure in the hanging-wall but retarding it in the footwall, and planes of weakness, are also factors for consideration.

The types of tensile failure shown in figure 54 should be helpful in recognizing similar failure in a mine where the intermediate principal stress can provide a friction to supplement any cohesion in resisting the opening of joint planes. These failure patterns are obtained with openings cut in 1/4-inch plates of Columbia resin (CR 39), a brittle plastic used in photoelastic studies. In each case, the specimens are loaded biaxially in compression on their edges. The vertical load varied up to 3500 psi, and the horizontal load between zero and 100 psi, as shown.

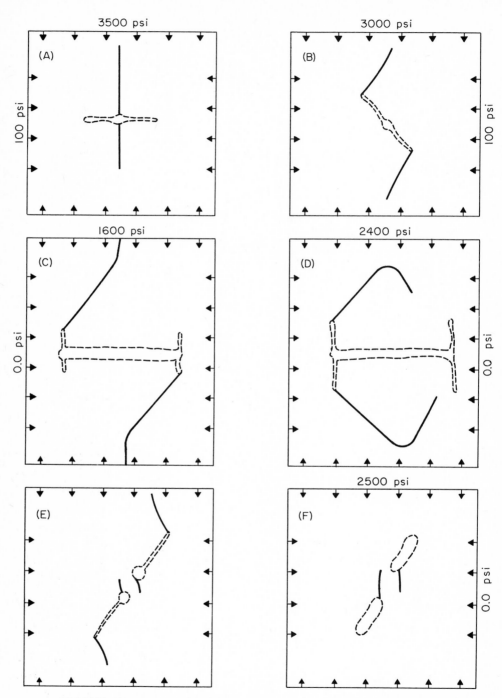

FIGURE 54 Tensile failure patterns. (*Courtesy of B. B. Dhar, McGill University*)

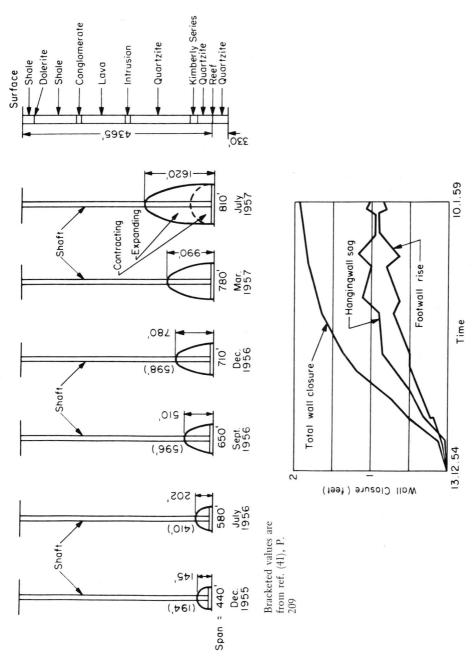

Bracketed values are
from ref. (41), P.
209

FIGURE 55 Displacements in the ventilation shaft, Harmony Gold Mine, South Africa. (Refs. 41, 65 and 66)

Loading a plate on edge after an opening has been cut in it probably places a different priority on types of failure than when the procedure is reversed, as is the case in a mine. Nevertheless, failure patterns of the two-dimensional laboratory type are of interest in a practical context.

In figures 54A and B tensile cracks are developed at the points of maximum tension shown in figure 28. Figures 54C and D simulate a horizontal stope with the so-called "free-shear" planes of figures 43 and 46 developed at each face. The suggestion is that as these planes develop in the face area the mechanics of failure swing more positively to tension at their tips. Figures 54E and F represent the possibility of tensile failure in pillar structures. Here, the tensile phase of Q (the minor principal stress) should be noted for ovaloids in figures 35, 37, and 39.

On the practical side, shafts and other permanent openings can be developed in a relaxing zone or they can be over-stoped to develop such a zone. The former is preferable but the latter is often the alternative available. Before theory adequately covered the point the effects of the relaxing zone were established empirically on the Kolar Gold Field. Here the main quartz lode, with a near-vertical dip, was frequently displaced 100 feet or more by folds pitching at about 60°. It was found that a raise on the nose of a fold permitted stoping the hangingwall limb as a means of de-stressing the footwall ground containing the remainder of the fold. The intermediate and footwall limbs were then mined in that order, generally free from pressure problems.

From the above and similar examples it has been established, for branching or parallel veins under pressure conditions, that mining should commence and continue on a single plane until a sufficient portion of the branching or parallel vein has been over-stoped to be included in the relaxing zone. At this stage stoping can commence in the relaxing zone on the branching or parallel structure and extend the original relaxing zone as it progresses.

A further application is available with wide orebodies if the advantages appear to justify the cost and inconvenience involved. This would provide for a hangingwall slot mined as narrow as possible, consistent with speed and cost. As this slot will attract most of the pressure problems, mining must follow a rigorous sequence to establish a continuous relaxing zone within which the footwall ore can be mined, generally free from pressure effects, except that the stability of transverse pillars in such ground would be related to the stress range involved in relaxation.

THE FRACTURE ZONE

A fracture zone develops with respect to an opening only as an extreme phase of and incidental to the process of decompression. It is frequently the only outward manifestation of the compression and relaxing zones and until it develops the ground is self-supporting.

The "free shear," characteristic of failure in the compression zone, and the varieties of tensile failure possible in the relaxing zone have been referred to. These mechanisms, supplemented by gravitational body forces, weaknesses through the rock

mass, and the types of failure illustrated in figures 14 and 15 cover the basic mechanisms contributing to fracture zone development. There is free shear at the face,
a sagging of the hangingwall, and, in due course, probably a heaving of the footwall.
As the fracture zone develops, elastic recovery in the surrounding rock induces
secondary strains within the fractured material. These are reflected as compression,
including Voussoir thrusts, and a tendency towards differential movement. When
reinforced by effective support the trend is towards equilibrium between fracture,
relaxing zones, and compression zones. Thus, the earlier support is in place, the sooner
its contribution to ground control will be realized.

The distinction between shear and tensile failure in rocks is not particularly
obvious, though some crushing on the surface of a shear fracture should be apparent.
In general, tensile failure can be suspected when fractures are radial or, in some cases,
parallel to the surface of an excavation. Fractures at intermediate angles suggest
shearing as they could represent a compromise with the shear trajectories shown in
figure 45.

As rocks are weakest in tension, when possible, good design will avoid such
strains. However, when nature presents us with an intermediate principal stress which
can retard early failure along some jointing, the significance of tensile strains must not
be underestimated.

With tensile and compressive failure mechanisms in competition, the initial
failure to be observed in stope walls may well be tensile. Either type should develop
gradually with the extension of the stoping span. The gradual process, however, can be
compromised by variations in rock strength within the walls. At depth, when low stress
ratios and high axis ratios are involved, it is a mathematical certainty that failure will
develop ultimately either through tension or through shear. However, the degree to
which either mechanism is effective also depends upon the properties of the rock mass
with its associated weaknesses. The effect of the latter may be even more obvious than
that of stress distribution in determining the range and type of failure around mine
openings.

When an opening is made in a rock mass traversed by multiple parallel planes
of weakness such as pronounced bedding or schistosity, the relative strength along
these planes can be such that they take precedence in initiating failure, almost
regardless of the direction and magnitude of the stress field. In addition to contributing to gradual failure, over a range of stress patterns such weaknesses also exert a
control on the outline of the fracture zone to extend it in a direction normal to the
planes of weakness. This suggests that when openings conform in direction with such
planes, e.g. a shaft, the longer cross-sectional dimension should be normal to these
planes. Theoretical considerations also suggest that an opening in a rock mass not so
weakened would develop a fracture zone of similar outline if a greatly increased stress
was superimposed in a direction normal to the planes of weakness. There is thus an
interchangeability between the effects of stress and multiple parallel planes of
weakness.

Again, over a range of stress patterns a single major plane of weakness such as

FIGURE 56   FIGURE 57

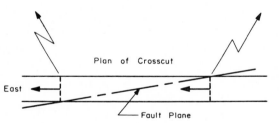

The Ooregum Gold Mining Co. of India Ltd., Bullen's 68th level Xcut

a fault or a contact acts as a discontinuity with a somewhat different effect. Figures 56 and 57 show the effect of a fault on the arching of a crosscut under the loading and rock conditions of a particular mine. It will be noted that the fault plane acting as a discontinuity forms the crown of the arch as long as the crosscut is directly within its sphere of influence and the outline of the arch varies with this control. Similar observations are so common in ground under pressure that we are justified in generalizing to the effect that providing the discontinuity is not normal to the direction of the major principal stress, other things being equal, it will tend to cause an irregularity in the outline of an otherwise normal fracture zone. Induced block caving and the cover caving of longwalling are examples of a progressively controlled fracture zone development and the mechanisms involved have a place in any general theory on the subject. In block caving, figure 30, the operation represents a vertically progressing fracture zone; to achieve this, controls are designed to eliminate any tendency towards a stable ellipsoid over the undercut. The development of a fracture zone below the undercut follows when stresses exceed rock strength enhanced by the dead weight of the ground involved.

Longwall operations should induce the most gradual stress changes, but once the longwalling of an area commences the gradual nature of failure at the face and over the back depends upon the degree of pressure and the properties of individual units in the geological succession. The general acceptability of longwalling implies that rocks, given the opportunity, will usually fail gradually rather than suddenly. This in turn implies sufficient pressure to ensure a state of incipient failure in the critical areas of any fracture zone. To explain sudden failure on a large scale we must look for obstructions to this gradual process. An obvious example is a rigidity in some member of the hangingwall or footwall succession which requires a greater axis ratio than others to generate critical stresses in either tension or compression.

THE DOME

This expression has a time-honoured, though often misinterpreted, place in the process of zone development. It can be regarded as that surface surrounding an excavation beyond which ground remains within the elastic limit and within which the elastic limit has been exceeded resulting in rupture. It is thus a factual, though poorly defined, surface separating any fracture zone from compression and relaxing zones.

Summary and Conclusions

The gravitational stress field is a fact of mining but measurements to date suggest that stress distributions are usually more complicated. Loading history and / or tectonic processes no doubt are contributing factors. A more precise knowledge of the pre-mining stress distribution is thus desirable. For such measurements, strains within the elastic limit must be distinguished from all other displacements — a very difficult assignment.

The redistribution of stress trajectories, as a result of an opening, develops compression and relaxing zones based on the opening. These zones can exist only at the expense of some loss in the volume as excavated. This encroachment on the excavated volume is resisted by the properties of the rock mass and when elastic limits are exceeded rupture follows to develop a fracture zone. Failure in the compression zone is commonly in shear and, in particular, in "free shear." On the other hand, in the relaxing zone failure is usually first indicated by an opening of joint planes and separations along schistosity and bedding planes. Under other conditions, tensile failure, after the types shown in figure 54, is possible, particularly when an intermediate principal stress can increase friction and retard early failure along jointing.

As mining continues to extend the fracture zone, pressure resulting from the compression and relaxing zones is transferred gradually to the fractured material. This induces secondary strains including Voussoir thrusts within the fracture zone. With these, supplemented by effective support, there is a trend towards equilibrium of forces.

Any shrinkage in excavated volume related to the compression zone must be transferred to surface within elastic limits as subsidence of a very low order, figure 53.

The Dome is defined as the surface surrounding an excavation beyond which the elastic limit has been retained, but within which it has been exceeded resulting in rupture.

The numerous assumptions introduced throughout the studies limit the generality of results. Nevertheless, these results approximate conditions experienced in practice with sufficient accuracy to justify the following conclusions for practical purposes:

1. The maximum compressive and tensile stress concentrations, as a result of an excavation, occur at the surface of the opening and are a function of its shape (geometry) and the nature of the initial stress field.

2. The depth of sensibly abnormal stress surrounding an excavation depends upon the size of the excavation and usually is less than one or two times the greatest cross-sectional dimension normal to the length. High stress concentrations rapidly taper off as indicated in the various illustrations.

3. Insofar as mine openings approximate ellipses, figure 28 summarizes the trend in tangential stress concentrations on the surface of ellipses with variations in the axis ratio, in the stress ratio and in the inclination of the axis of the ellipse with respect to the stress axis. Conditions producing high compressive stresses are to be noted as well as those resulting in variations between tension and compression.

4. In the foregoing studies, stresses within the elastic limit have been assumed. In actual practice when ground pressure approaches the strength of the rock, openings with shapes related to the higher critical stresses are likely to work themselves, through failure in tension or shear, to forms inducing lower stress concentrations. The effective outline to regain stability would be a compromise between the effects of the stress ratio, rock properties and weaknesses through the rock mass to give stresses below critical values. This stable outline will lie somewhere between the "as-cut" outline and an ultimate (elliptical) outline which results in a uniform stress around the surface of the opening. This occurs when the opening has worked itself so that the major elliptical axis is parallel to the major principal stress and the axis ratio is the reciprocal of the stress ratio. The condition represents the ultimate stable shape and if the rock strength is less than this uniform stress value the ground cannot carry a self-supporting opening. (See figure 28, sub-figures H, L, and P, also figure 52C.)

5. Sharp corners are zones of high stress concentration where failure in shear is likely to be conspicuous.

6. Pillars are natural concentrators of stress and when mining provides for geometrically spaced pillar support, other things being equal, as the opening-to-

pillar-width ratio increases, the average shear stress in the pillars increases at a more rapid rate than the maximum shear stress. For large values of opening-to-pillar-width ratio (above 75 per cent recovery), the maximum and average shear stress concentrations are nearly equal.

For recoveries of less than 60 per cent, the rate of change of the average compressive stress concentration with per cent recovery is small, and for recoveries exceeding 60 per cent, when pillars carry the full superincumbent load, this rate of change is large. The average compressive stress concentration in the final stages of pillar recovery increases without limit, figure 42, but pillar failure is the limiting condition. When pillar dimensions are fairly uniform, pillars in the centre of a stoping area are likely to show greater strain than those nearer the boundaries of the area.

7. Variations in the minor principal stress between tension and compression in the vicinity of a pillar structure, for various conditions of loading, are shown in Figures 34 to 39 (60). The shear stresses also require consideration.

8. The stress distributions described are based on elastic theory and disregard body forces or dead weight. These latter, initiating falls of ground, are an outstanding cause of mine accidents.

3 | Ground Control Facilities

Ground control problems have many aspects but two principles only are involved. The ground surrounding mining excavations must be retained rigidly in place or it must be induced to rupture under a degree of control which invites gradual failure. These principles are represented by rigid pillar and longwall methods. In the former a rigidity in supports is implied but in the latter a degree of compressibility is essential. Between the best ground conditions for each principle there is a gray zone where a choice in principles is difficult. With the advent of rockbursts the trend is towards the longwall sequence. In the case of gradual failure, however, a sophisticated judgement is required to decide when deteriorating ground conditions, and the consequential loss in efficiency, justify the transition to a longwall sequence.

Rigid Pillar Methods

These methods imply that with pillar support, the main roof or hangingwall (and footwall) is retained rigidly in place to protect the workings and to secure the surface or some intermediate horizon. Further support (or ground control) is limited to that which is necessary as a protection against local rock falls.

The methods include conventional room and pillar layouts on flat dips and the crown, sill, and rib pillar layouts of steeper dips. They provide for a geometric arrangement of rooms and pillars. The rooms (or stopes) are mined leaving the pillars as general support for the operation, figures 58 and 59. The pillars are permanent support insofar as the stability of the surface is a dominating factor, or they are temporary support pending a pillar recovery operation. Either alternative demands an average loading on pillars which is well within the competency of the rock involved. This aspect is discussed later under "support in mines."

When an early pillar recovery operation is provided for, the time element

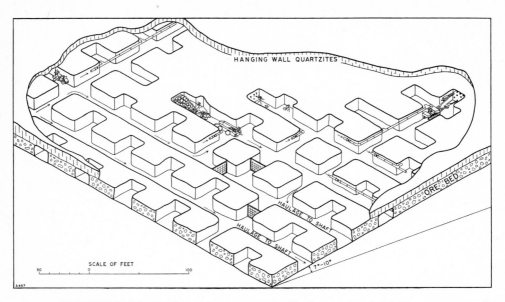

FIGURE 58 Idealized trackless room-and-pillar layout, Stanleigh Uranium Mines[68]

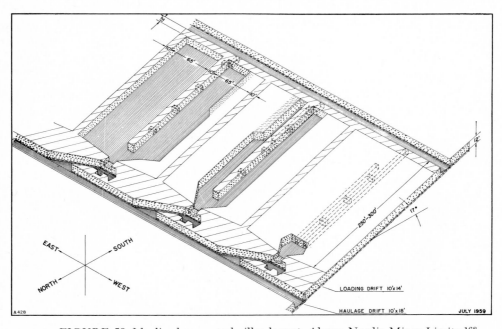

FIGURE 59 Idealized room-and-pillar layout, Algom Nordic Mines Limited[68]

may permit some variation in the factor of safety on pillar strength. As noted later, under pillar design, the larger the breadth to width ratio the stronger the pillar. This also invites judgement as to the factor of safety, but with depth the percentage of pillar support required reaches prohibitive proportions and longwall alternatives become competitive.

In the transition from rigid pillar to longwall methods, quite independent of the dip the proportion of pillar support also can be varied downwards to ensure that pillar failure follows at a safe distance behind the working faces. In such cases the proportion of ore left as pillars may not justify a separate recovery operation. Such pillars constitute a very temporary support and to achieve the objective of gradual failure, working faces are placed on a modified longwall sequence. Thus room and pillar and longwall principles merge on a time basis. The working face is largely dependent on pillar support, but ground conditions in the mine as a whole depend upon the longwall principle of gradual failure, figure 61.

Longwall Methods — Sequential Mining

Longwall methods originated in coal mining and refer to the practice of carrying a long straight working face paralleling or at a convenient angle to the dip, figure 60. Faces run to 500 feet or more in length and offer certain advantages in the use of mechanical equipment.

A further outstanding advantage is the degree of control possible over the roof and floor. With longwalling, subsidence in coal measures is predictable to a high degree, due largely to the gradual, continuous, and orderly shifting of pressure with the

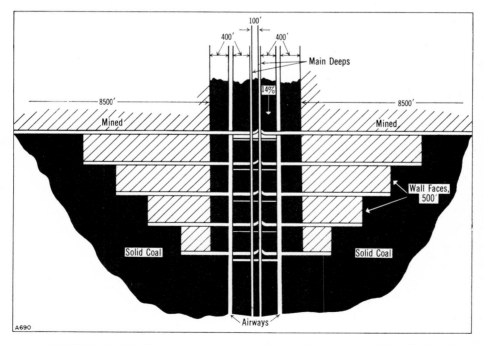

FIGURE 60 Idealized plan of advancing longwall operation. (*After United States Bureau of Mines, I.C. 7698*)

progress of the face, removing 100 per cent of the coal and leaving no pillars in its path for subsequent recovery.

The principle implies sufficient pressure to ensure a gradual failure and for this purpose the method of support is secondary to the order in which the ground is removed. With such faces always working towards the solid, stress concentrations associated with pillars are avoided and as a result of gradual failure the whole operation proceeds under a more or less uniform and consistent stress distribution at the working face. The stoping area can be extended as a single continuous opening, and the ground is thus given every opportunity for gradual rather than sudden failure. Longwalling in panels separated by large pillars is a special case, limiting tensile strains in the floor and back.

In metal mining practice the term "longwalling" is extended beyond coal mine usage to include any sequence of stope faces the orderly progress of which will remove, overcut, or undercut 100 per cent of the ore on a continuous plane. The long face is usually broken into shorter lengths disposed to conform with the stoping method, but the faces are kept in sequence to give a modified form of longwall, figure 61. In the process, predictable failure conditions are induced by eliminating or minimizing stress concentrations due to pillars, remnants, and / or structural discontinuities. For our less rigorous use of the term, sequential mining might be more appropriate than longwalling, but unfortunately the latter terminology has long usage in its favour.

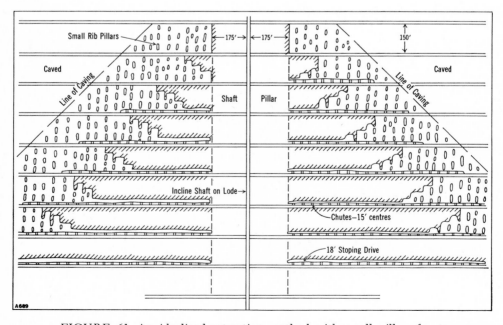

FIGURE 61 An idealized retreating method with small pillars for temporary support, Michigan copper area[68]

In detail there are many variations of longwalling, but in general five options only are available. The orebody may be opened out from the top down, from the bottom up, from one or other of the lateral boundaries, or outwards from a point within the orebody, figure 62. Some form of longwalling is essential in rockburst country and offers many advantages in deep mining generally when gradual failure only is anticipated.

A modified longwall principle can be associated with any stoping method regardless of dip, but serves little purpose when there is adequate rigid pillar support. The practice can be carried out either as an advancing or as a retreating operation. In advancing, levels must be maintained through stoped ground and level maintenance can be expensive. In retreating, the stoped level can be abandoned as the stope progresses. Access is through a level in the solid ore and level support may be required only for the working face and its approaches. In rockburst country there is much in favour of retreating, but the advantage of either alternative is usually a matter of economics rather than of safety.

With these explanations, under obvious pressure conditions a very simple principle requires examination. In the initial state an orebody is intact and subjected only to the pre-mining field stress. In the final stage of mining, regardless of the method, the removal of 100 per cent of the ore has left an excavation surrounded by a fracture zone subjected to varying stress concentrations on its periphery, the magnitudes of which are related to the geometry of its outline. The ground control objective is to proceed from the initial to the final state with the minimum possible variation in stress concentration. That this objective can be achieved only through the application of longwall principles and the necessary supporting facilities can be demonstrated by any acceptable method of stress analysis. Under these circumstances, with failure conditions in either tension or compression inherent throughout the operation, absolute stress measurements are seldom of more than academic interest.

On the other hand the limitations of the method must be recognized. The control introduced with longwalling is that of gradual stress change. Exceptions will arise where the gradual failure required for stability in the rock mass does not follow the gradual stress change. This introduces an unpredictable element which for open stoping may limit the application of the method. Each case represents a special problem, but there are some alternatives including mining panels isolated by large pillars and / or the early placement of fill.

In ground control we can refer to "tactics" as the short term objective concerned with the support and advance of individual working faces — the mining method. "Strategy" then becomes the long term objective concerned with the relationship of mining openings to each other and to ground conditions in the mine as a whole — the mining sequences and overall stability.

In large orebodies tactics can then proceed without reference to strategy for the mining of up to fifty per cent of an orebody. However, ultimate ground conditions, and thus ore recovery and cost, in mining the remaining ore will be strongly influenced by the strategy introduced with the earliest mining.

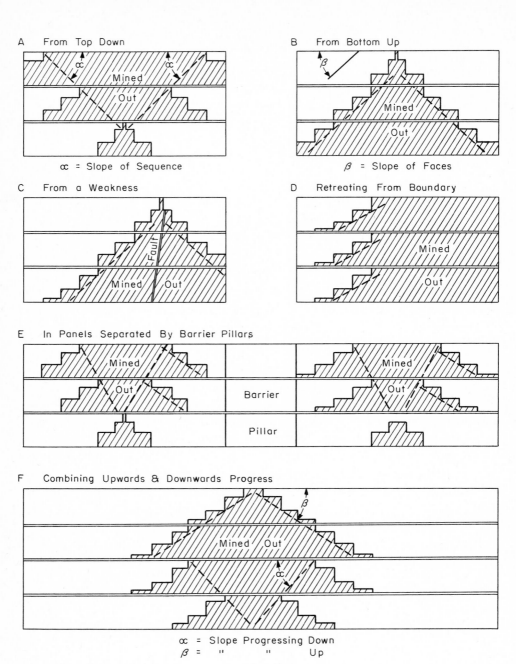

FIGURE 62 Longwall sequence possibilities

Support in Stopes

The objectives of ground control have been stated as either to retain the ground surrounding mining excavations rigidly in place or to induce gradual failure and control its progress within the limits of safe operating conditions. In either case a degree of predictability is implied which is obtained by mining sequences and / or various methods and types of support.

The supporting problem involves both static loads related to ground pressure and the dead weight of fractured rock and dynamic loads arising from sudden failure and its associated seismic activity. It ranges from the general, concerned with the broad aspects of mine stability, to the specific, concerned with the details of local ground failure and safety. Over this range practice develops as a compromise between supporting and operating requirements and facilities.

Shafts, levels, raises, chambers, and stopes all present somewhat different supporting problems, in each case strongly influenced by economic aspects. These aspects are related to ore grades, wage rates, and the cost of supporting materials. They may demand variations in practice from camp to camp, but principles have a universal application.

Reference has been made to stress zones, fracture zones, and relaxed zones. Each contributes to a contraction of the excavation. With small openings at shallow depth the process may not be significant, but the effect varies exponentially with increasing span, and with increased ground pressure due to depth or other causes, it can be critical as regards support. Experience has established that contraction of the opening to some degree is unavoidable. Thus rigid support, less competent than that of the ground removed, carries the seeds of its own destruction, but a yielding or compressible support, while not preventing the process, can resist it indefinitely. Fortunately with most mining operations there is a gradualness in the transition from rigid to compressible requirements which permits time to adjust from one condition to the other.

Supporting practice represents one of the bridges between ground control and mining methods. The discussion which follows will be confined to supporting facilities most commonly available and to the more important principles relating to their application.

Stoping is the most active agency causing stress redistribution and this responds to the advance of the working face. With sufficient pressure, failure, usually in shear, follows the face and initiates the fracture zone already described. A yielding support such as fill has little initial effect on the stress distribution, but later may contribute substantially to the processes leading to stability.

With many mining methods the stability of the mine depends upon the effectiveness of the overall support. This introduces the idea of mass support. In addition, the safety of travelling ways and working faces will depend upon local support. This is achieved by what may be called unit types of support, the effects of which are usually limited to local areas.

MASS SUPPORT — PILLARS

Strength and Loading — Pillars are a mass type of support insofar as they contribute collectively to general mine stability. They are a unit type insofar as a tributary area depends upon each one for protection. As a mass support random or uniformly distributed pillars are the only means of ensuring rigidity in the rock mass as a whole. As a unit type of support their usefulness is usually of a temporary nature and provision for their recovery or gradual failure may be a feature of the mining method employed.

At depths of a few hundred feet, under gravity loading the strength of brittle rocks relative to the loading is usually so great that a small percentage of pillar support ensures adequate ground stability. For this reason pillars as a method of support have become universally acceptable in this depth range. At greater depths, however, pressure effects have created serious problems. We can thus generalize to the effect that pillars have an undisputed place in any supporting system as long as their loading can be maintained within safe limits or their gradual failure can be predicted. With increasing depth or tectonic stresses the first requirement becomes difficult, and a condition arises where rigid pillars can be justified only after a consideration of the risks involved.

Design Principles — Due to the variables which enter every situation there is still a range of opinion as to both the strength and the loads carried by pillars. Coates (2, 67) and also Obert and Duvall (3) have developed interesting approaches to both problems and a photoelastic study of pillar loading has been given earlier. The tributary area approach which follows (68) serves to indicate some of the variables involved.

Consider a horizontal pillar-supported mining area. If the mined area is extensive enough, with gravity loading only, some pillars ultimately must carry the full superincumbent load. Assuming a uniform distribution over similar pillars and neglecting sidewall effects on the periphery of the mining area, this average load can be expressed as follows. For other than gravity loading, the problem is more complicated.

$$\sigma_p = \frac{Dd}{144} \left\{ \frac{A}{a} \right\} \qquad (1)$$

σ_p = average pillar loading (psi)
d = density (lbs. per cubic foot)
D = depth below surface (feet)
A = area supported by pillars (feet^2)
a = area of pillars (feet^2)

In concrete and other test work compressive strength, over some range, has been found to bear a relationship to specimen width (W) to height (H) ratio. Lacking a better yardstick, when C represents the compressive strength of a specimen with a W / H ratio of 1.0 the strength for other ratios has been expressed as follows (68):

$$S = C\sqrt{\frac{W}{H}} \qquad (2)$$

For ready reference, pillar dimensions may be defined as follows: Length (L) is the greater and breadth (B) the smaller dimension in the plane of the lode. Width (T) is the dimension from hangingwall to footwall or from roof to floor.

Insofar as we are justified in transposing laboratory test results into the practical field, to apply with small pillars formula (2) may be written.

$$S_p = C\sqrt{\frac{B}{T}} = \text{strength of pillar} \qquad (3)$$

On this basis the following is a suggested procedure for determining the C factor above. Figure 63 gives a frequency distribution of some 300 compressive strength determinations for a single rock type, Elliot Lake conglomerate, with values based on a width to height ratio of 1.0. The mean value is 26,600 psi and the standard

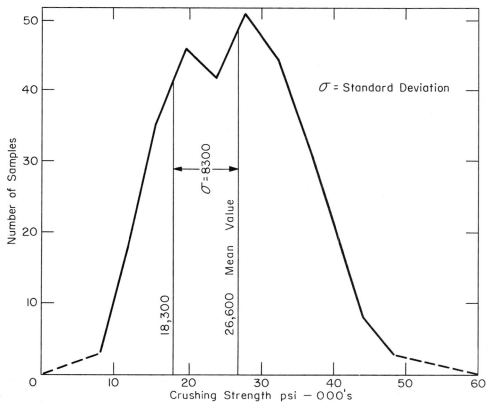

FIGURE 63 Frequency distribution of test values for an Elliot Lake conglomerate

deviation for all values is 8300 psi. Similar results could probably have been obtained from thirty to forty representative test samples. As a Gaussian distribution is approximated, the mean value (26,600) less one standard deviation (8300) gives a value of 18,300 psi above which 84 per cent of all subsequent values can be expected to fall. This will be referred to as the *specified strength*. The C factor would be derived by dividing this specified strength by a suitable factor of safety to provide for variations in stress distribution, size, time, and other effects involved in transposing laboratory results to the practical field. Static loading only is involved and judgement enters into the selection of this factor of safety. If 4 is selected, the C factor then would be 18,300 / 4, approximately 4600 psi. This would represent the safe average load for a rock pillar of B / T ratio of 1.0, on a horizontal plane giving a factor of safety of 5.8 on the mean value of 26,600 psi.

An application of the above for horizontal workings is given in figure 64 which sets out, for one rock type, the calculated minimum percentage of pillar support permissible and the loading for different depths and B / T ratios, assuming that the relationships of formula (3) apply and that the pillars ultimately carry the full superincumbent load.

With sufficient area, in horizontal deposits under gravity loading σ_p of formula (1) can be equated with S_p of formula (3). Thus

$$C\sqrt{\frac{B}{T}} = \frac{Dd}{144}\left\{\frac{A}{a}\right\} \qquad (4)$$

Such a relationship provides a guide for design purposes but its limitations, including any distinction between average and maximum loads, must not be overlooked.

Hedley and Grant (69), in the light of more recent experience, have revised and extended formulae for small pillars in reference (68). Their C factor is based on a crushing strength of 26,000 psi for a one foot cube as compared with 26,600 psi for a drill core specimen with a diameter / height ratio of 1.0 in reference (68). They also include a density factor of 160 lbs / ft³, a pre-mining horizontal stress normal to the strike of 3000 psi and the following additional notation to arrive at the formulae given below.

$$S_p = \frac{26,000 \times B^{.5}}{T^{.75}} = \text{strength of pillar.}$$

$$\sigma_p = \frac{1.1 \, D \cos^2 d + 3000 \sin^2 d}{1 - R}$$

R = extraction ratio = area mined / area of orebody

d = dip of orebody

A factor of safety = S_p / σ_p = 1.5 appears to separate stable from uncertain conditions.

In coal mining, Holland (70), Salamon (71, 72), and Bieniawski (73) have developed formulae for pillar strength which vary from the above in the C factor

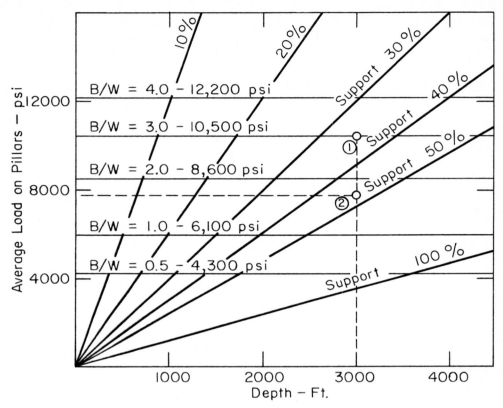

FIGURE 64 Safe Loads on Pillars —
Varying Extraction
Ratios

Specific strength 18,300 psi.
Density 170 lb/ft.³ = 1.2 psi/ft.
factor of safety = 3.0

Examples
1) Depth 3,000′ B/T ratio = 3.0.
    Safe load of 10,500 psi is
    obtained with 34% support.

2) As above but factor of safety
    of 4.0. Safe load of 7,900 psi
    is obtained with 45% support.

and / or the powers used in the B / T ratio. Wilson and Ashwin (74), also in coal
mining, divide the area of the pillar into a yield zone and an elastic core. A formula is
then derived for the stability of the pillar based on the loading of the core.

The foregoing discussion emphasizes tributary areas, size effects, B / T ratios,
extraction ratios, and average loading. These are important in pillar design insofar as
they reflect critical shear stresses. It has been suggested that free shear was a type of
failure characteristic of compression zones, of which pillars are the extreme example.
From the rounding of sharp corners at the hanging and foot walls, to the development

of an hour-glass outline, this type of failure is prominent in pillars loaded to critical values. It is related to the maximum skin stress at the pillar surface with which the average stress may vary considerably.

There are practical reasons for believing that pillar-supporting capacity deteriorates with time. Whether this is due to weakening or to increased loading is not definitely known, but, with time, loads may shift from smaller to larger pillars.

With the additional restraint provided with increasing pillar breadth there is a trend from limited towards infinite strength for pillars of great breadth. However, failure conditions are conspicuous on the pillar surface and in openings through heavily loaded pillars and in brittle ground rockbursts are not uncommon.

As the dip increases, the gravitational stress is resolved into a decreasing normal stress on the pillar, an increasing shearing stress parallel to the pillar contact and a steepening stress gradient between maximum tension and maximum compression. Thus for pillars in inclined deposits, planes of weakness parallel to the dip assume greater significance and pillars with their length parallel to the dip thus have advantages.

For inclined deposits under a gravity load, Figure 54F also suggests the possibility of tensile failure on horizontal pillar faces.

The room and pillar layouts of flat dips are maintained with modification on steeper dips by the use of conventional sill, crown and rib pillars, figure 97.

For the purpose of these notes, a *sill pillar* represents any ground left standing horizontally between the level and the stope floor above. A *crown pillar* represents the ground left standing horizontally between the level and the completed back of the stope below. *Rib pillars* are those with their length in the direction of the dip, designed to limit stoping spans and to support the walls.

The function of the above pillars, as on flatter dips, is to provide the major ground control necessary for the stoping operation. Their dimensions, within trial and error limits, are a matter of convenience and are referred to also under various mining methods. When planning provides for their recovery this should follow at the earliest opportunity as the effects of further loading and time are uncertain factors.

Mining Spans — Room and pillar operations are laid out to leave a proportion of the ore as uniformly distributed rigid pillar support, the proportion being expressed as a percentage of the whole. The percentage is determined by empiricism, by calculation, or more commonly by intuition related to both. Pillar dimensions and the spans between pillars must then be established. The B / T ratio and its effect on pillar strength has been referred to. The operator naturally reaches for the highest ratio possible, but this depends upon a compromise with mining spans because for a given percentage extraction, the greater the ratio, the greater the span. It is to be noted also that for a given percentage of pillar support a square-pillar pattern involves shorter spans than a rib-pillar pattern.

Ground competence is dependent on the rock type, structure, and loading conditions. With bedded deposits beam and plate theories have been applied to

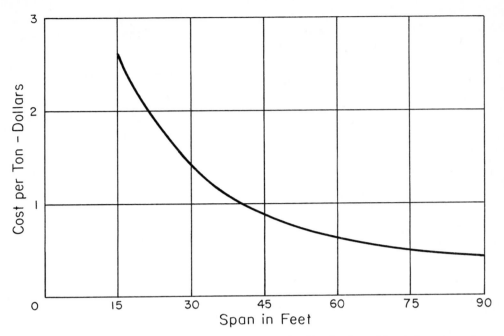

FIGURE 65 The effect of stoping span on the distribution of fixed charges per ton; based on stope length 200 ft., height 8 ft., and fixed charges of $5,200 per raise.

this is the 1/X curve,

$$= \frac{a \ fixed \ cost}{variable \ tonnage}$$

calculate safe operating spans. The U.S. Bureau of Mines has made notable contributions in this respect (75, 76, 77, 78). However, the validity of such calculations must be confined to the range of elastic theory. Elastic theory in mine stress distribution has an application only with unruptured rock which exists beyond the limits of any fracture zone. Beams of finite depth develop only as a part of a fracture zone, within which extreme caution is essential in the application of any strength theories. Nevertheless, tempered with a high degree of empiricism such calculations can provide useful guidance.

The optimum span within a given geological context is a compromise between working facilities, development costs, and other economic aspects. The economic aspects usually refer to a fixed cost distributed over the tonnage to be mined from different spans. This results in the 1 / X relationship between span and tonnage where 1 is the fixed cost and X the variable tonnage, figure 65.

Figure 65 represents a special case from the Elliot Lake mines (68) where $5200 represented the fixed cost of stope preparation regardless of span, with stope lengths of 200 feet on dip and height (width) 8 feet. The graph indicates that beyond a span on strike of 45 feet, costs per ton decrease very slowly. On the other hand, risks are probably rising to the degree where little is to be gained in reaching for a maximum span.

Again referring to early Elliot Lake operations, in a succession of conglomerates and quartzites and the mining by room and pillar of 25,000,000 tons of ore from orebodies some 10 feet thick and dipping about 17°, figure 66 represents the range of stoping spans related to depth actually found in practice (68). This is based on good rock-bolting practice but no external support between pillars.

As the pillar height, roof to floor, increases or the dip steepens, pillar dimensions without reference to loading must first ensure the integrity of the pillar under its own deadweight and jointing characteristics. In these cases, theoretical considerations

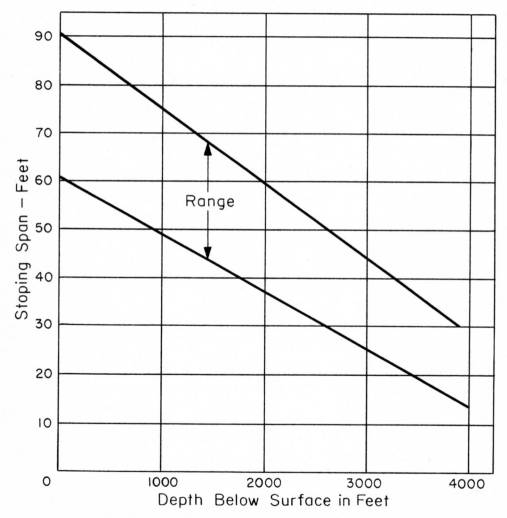

FIGURE 66 Relationship between depth and unsupported stoping span

are largely displaced by empiricism. This is usually the case in flat orebodies involving high pillars and on steep dips involving sill, crown, and rib pillars. Except for the rib pillar, on steep dips spans between pillars are determined by the level interval and other prior design considerations. When ground stress proves excessive for such spans a mining layout offering better control is indicated.

Temporary Pillars — As noted earlier, there is usually a time effect involved in rock failure. Frequently there is also a time factor associated with the usefulness of pillars. This will vary from the long-term stability demanded when support of the surface or intermediate horizons is the critical factor, to the short term stability required in the vicinity of a working face. In the first case, the formulae given for pillar strength and loading are a useful guide. In the latter case pillar failure can follow the advance of the working face, figure 61, and a lower percentage of pillar support is required. This percentage can be determined only by a process of trial and error.

All methods demanding a pillar-recovery operation fall between these extremes. The data available permits little accuracy in the interpretation of time strains which may be either plastic or elastic. For this reason, the layout which provides for the earliest recovery of pillars, once their usefulness has passed, is likely to be the most satisfactory. This generalization applies particularly to open-stope methods where the grade of ore precludes the use of fill. Pillar robbing is to be distinguished from pillar recovery and follows as the end phase of an operation which still requires pillar support.

Shaft Pillars — These pillars are designed to protect a shaft, either inclined or vertical, from the effects of stoping in its vicinity. As large B / T ratios are involved the design is more closely related to empiricism than to the general principles of pillar loading and strength outlined above. Stability at the surface is a consideration, but security and reasonable maintenance costs for the shaft and other openings in the pillar are also requirements. This demands low stress concentrations.

The use of a shaft pillar involves removing from production for an indefinite period such ore as may be included in its design. At times this may be a prohibitive requirement and in such cases, with a smaller pillar, the shaft would be regarded as expendable and its ultimate security merged with other uncertainties of the future.

Numerous rules have been developed for estimating the size of shaft pillars, but their usefulness in most cases has been confined to the area in which they originated. Good design must assess the possibilities of alternative locations and the economics of deferred production. Angles of draw and break are also important factors. Nevertheless, there is little precision entering into design principles and empiricism is likely to be the final guide.

Within this limitation the principles embodied in O'Donahue's rules have survived in the literature since 1907. He postulated an angle of draw of 8° for horizontal strata. This angle, determined in coal mining practice prior to 1907, is perhaps not comparable with present angles of draw resulting from more precise measurements. However, it could approximate an angle of break below which serious damage to a shaft would follow. For inclined deposits he assumed a greater angle of draw to the dip side than to the rise side of underground excavations which is still generally agreed to. His rules for an 8° angle of draw for horizontal deposits have been incorporated in Statham's (79) formulae designed to cover any angle of draw as follows:

1. For the upper side of a pillar the angle of draw (θ) to an inclination of 24° is as in figure 67:

$$\theta = a + \left\{ \frac{24 - a}{24} \right\} d$$

a = angle of draw in horizontal strata

d = inclination of seam in degrees

For steeper dips the angle of draw is estimated as 16° plus 0.3 times the angle of inclination of the seam to a maximum value of 37° which occurs at an inclination of 70° from the horizontal.

2. For the lower side of the pillar the angle of draw is

$$\theta = a - \left\{ \frac{a}{24} \right\} d, \text{ to a limiting value of } 0°$$

Alternatively, Professor J. T. Whetton, sometime Head of the Department of Mining, Leeds University, regards the rules of the Dortmund Board of Mines as the least compromising and most direct method of computing the size of a pillar in coal measure rocks (personal communication, 1960). These more conservative rules are indicated in figure 68.

In South Africa, where there is much experience in shaft pillar design in hard rocks, there is support for the empirical rule that a horizontal shaft pillar should have a diameter equivalent to one fifth of the depth (80). This postulates a design angle of draw of about 6 degrees, as compared with O'Donahue's 8 degrees, for horizontal coal measures. A similar rule for inclined deposits suggests a protecting cylinder around the shaft at any horizon, the diameter of which is some function of the depth as above. As a tribute to the greater angle of draw (break) on the up-dip side of such a pillar the shaft intersection should be in the lower portion.

With the essential factors for design purposes uncertain, if a shaft pillar can be avoided there are strong economic reasons for doing so. Cases will arise where the risks favour such a pillar but there is usually a limiting pillar size beyond which the shaft becomes expendable. This size will be strongly influenced by the value of the ore involved and angles of break or draw can seldom be adequately provided for. Orebodies, in such cases, are usually extensive in the plane of the lode, but ore widths are narrow and the amount of subsidence is thus limited. Under such conditions there is a school of thought which considers that at depths greater than 5000 feet the pillar breadth need not exceed 1000 feet though the length may be somewhat greater if the angle of draw from the up-dip face of the pillar is a factor.

With such a pillar, break or draw lines may intersect the shaft, but the

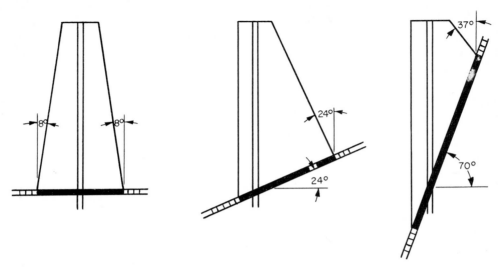

FIGURE 67 Shaft pillars. (*After Statham*[79])

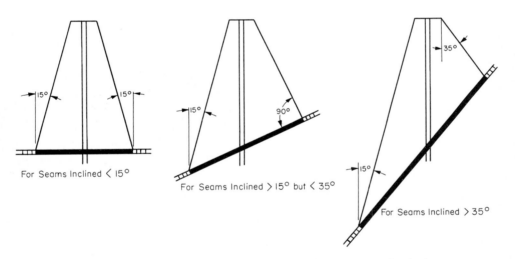

For Seams Inclined < 15°

For Seams Inclined > 15° but < 35°

For Seams Inclined > 35°

FIGURE 68 Shaft pillars. (*After Whetton, private communication*)

amount of movement involved should be tolerable. Such a pillar also has the advantage of approximating infinite strength, but the stress distribution must be such that boundary conditions and the maintenance of openings through it are not likely to be a serious problem.

With dips below 60 degrees an inclined shaft may have advantages and the problem of its protection and maintenance will arise. At one time for such a shaft in close proximity to the lode, a pillar was the accepted form of protection, figure 61. The size of the pillar, influenced by short term considerations, was frequently reduced to a degree where, over the long term, costly maintenance was involved.

Again South African experience has established that if the initial stoping is over the inclined shaft area, by eliminating any pillar the de-stressed (relaxing) zone following the stoping soon envelops the shaft and comparatively stable conditions follow. If this initial stoping can be carried out prior to sinking the shaft, any pressure problem is reduced to a minimum. This practice is in step with a trend towards relying less and less on pillar support at depth when other alternatives are reasonably available.

In this connection the effect of understoping the Harmony ventilation shaft in South Africa with the first stoping is illustrated in figure 55. This experience suggests that in many cases it may also be possible to eliminate a vertical shaft pillar.

Barrier Pillars — These are an essential feature of many mining operations when it is desired to operate more than one stoping sequence, to limit ground failure, to protect the surface or upper horizons, or to control the flow of water.

In extensive orebodies, forced through pressure conditions to longwall operations the rate of output can be greatly increased by the introduction of substantial barrier pillars to subdivide the orebody into panels which can be mined in sequences independent of each other, figure 62E. When we consider that at 15 per cent compound interest, profits accruing 15 years hence are worth only 12 cents on the dollar today, the risk of the complete loss of the ore involved in such pillars may well be justified, but in practice this seldom follows.

Enough has been given on pillar design to indicate the problems involved. Design principles are important, but the best answers are likely to arise when they have been supplemented by shrewd judgement based on experience.

MASS SUPPORT — FILLING METHODS

Waste and Hydraulic Fill — Open stoping, as the term implies, requires ground which will stand over working spans with little or no support. Such support as is required in travelling ways and at the face is provided by unit types with which small pillars, designed for failure, are included.

At shallow depths open stoping methods have a wide application, but with the advent of ground pressure, all ground loses its self-supporting ability and develops sloughing characteristics in varying degrees. This results in fracture zones, rock falls, and occasionally in pillar failure. In very narrow orebodies, the situation usually can be controlled with unit-type supports in longwall stopes progressing in a sequence. Some of the world's deepest mining is of this type. With increasing ore widths the situation is less amenable to this form of support and on the steeper dips filled stope methods of mining are the alternative. Some unit types of support are still required to protect the face and access ways, but the filling, while providing local support, also ensures mine stability and in steeply dipping stopes provides a working floor for operations.

With filling methods, pillars have little long-term significance in the supporting picture though they still may have a function as barriers sectionalizing the mine, as ribs separating stopes, and over a limited pressure range, as crowns and sills.

With these methods on steep dips, a stope is silled out either at or above the level and timbered backs or sill pillars to carry the fill are provided. The broken ore is drawn off the level below through ore passes carried upwards through the fill and fill is run in from the level above.

The filling material is a matter of local availability. Development waste, sand, gravel, and unclassified mill tailings have all been used. In exceptional cases, waste rock has been mined in special stopes or open pits for this purpose. Such material was difficult to place in orebodies dipping below the angle of repose. For steeper dips efficient distribution usually demanded a waste pass system from surface to the deepest stoping. From the waste pass to disposal in the stopes also required both tramming and scraping and costs reflected the man-hours involved (81).

Hydraulic fill of various types has been used extensively in flat-lying deposits, but its use in steeply dipping deposits was limited due to difficulties in transport, to the development of hydraulic pressure after the fill was placed, and to the problem of containment generally. A later development in the form of classified mill tailings has largely overcome these difficulties.

In the development of hydraulic fill it was found that sizing was important and also that slimes should be kept within definite limits for the best flow, drainage, and settling characteristics. For stope filling, a minimum percolation rate is desirable to facilitate drainage and thus prevent the build-up of hydraulic pressure in the fill. Such a risk is present with excessive slime.

The development of the Dutch State Cone and its numerous modifications provided an economical means of classifying mill tailings for filling purposes. When mixed with water and passed through such cones sufficient sliming material can be readily removed to give the remainder an acceptable percolation rate. The proportion and screen analysis of useful tailings remaining depends upon the mill grind, but generally after one or more stages of classification 40 to 60 per cent remained with a screen analysis which ensured a percolation rate suitable for filling purposes. Most mines have a mill producing tailings and their classification provides a readily available supporting medium.

The following are characteristic screen analyses from the International Nickel Company of Canada, Limited (82):

Percolation Rates					
SCREEN MESH	+65 PER CENT	−65 +200 PER CENT	−200 +800 PER CENT	−800 PER CENT	PERCOLATION RATE INCHES/HR.
Mill tailings	13.8	33.4	32.8	20.0	5.0
Sand fill (optimum)	9.2	67.0	20.9	2.9	5.0
Sand fill Frood-Stobie	23.1	45.7	26.7	3.5	5.0
Sand fill Creighton	39.1	43.6	12.5	4.8	3.5
Sand fill Levack	21.3	44.1	30.1	4.5	4.0

The range of acceptable screen analysis is indicated by a comparison of the above with the following data from the Kerr Addison Mine (83). Here 50 per cent of the mill tailings (cyanidation) are recovered by classification to give a percolation rate of 4 inches per hour.

Classified Tailings—Product and Reject Kerr Addison Mine, Virginiatown, Ont.					
Screen mesh	+65	+100	+200	−200	−325
Tailings	0.1	0.5	16.4	83.0	66.8
Product (sands)	0.2	1.4	33.2	65.2	36.4
Reject (slimes)	—	—	0.2	99.8	99.3

The sand product is pulped to a density of about 60 per cent solids by weight for distribution to the mine. The mine distribution system consists of bore holes when possible and pipe lines which are rubber lined in the more critical sections. The system represents a free flow from feed end to discharge and valves in the line can be a liability. The filling cycle in stopes both overhand and underhand is as follows, indicating the need for an effective signalling system, telephones being almost essential.

When the fencing to contain the fill has been placed and lined with burlap to retain the solids and permit drainage, water is called for. When a full flow of water indicates a clear line the water is displaced at the feed end of the system by the pulped fill which is placed in the stope as desired through hose connections. With slimes largely removed settlement is rapid and the surface water is decanted through raises to the mine drainage system below. When the required fill has been placed, pulp is displaced by water at the feed end until the line again runs clear when the water is closed off. The cycle is then complete leaving the excess water to be drained and pumped to surface. The normal stope cycle then follows on succeeding shifts. In settling, the fill retains sufficient moisture to give it some cohesion.

The initial resistance to wall closure and fracture zone development with any filling medium is limited, but builds up rapidly as wall closure develops. Thus it follows that the earlier fill is placed the sooner its resisting quality becomes effective. The best filling medium is that which can be placed with fewest voids and in this respect classified tailings have a prominent place.

A substantial capital charge is involved in installing the facilities for classified hydraulic fill. However, when required in sufficient quantity the overall advantages, including cost of placing such fill, are usually much more favourable than with other methods. As a result the method enjoys wide acceptability in both overhand and underhand practice.

Consolidating Fill — Sulphide mines usually carry a proportion of pyrrhotite in their ore. Pyrrhotite oxidizes very readily, giving off heat and setting up a cementing reaction. A proportion of pyrrhotite thoroughly mixed with a coarse fill, on oxidation, will result in an aggregate with a marked cohesion. After several months of oxidation, drifts can be driven through it with no support. The following fill as used at Noranda's Horne Mine (84) is mixed at the top of the fill raise for distribution in any particular area.

	PERCENTAGE
Slag from reverberatories granulated in water	72
Slag reclaimed from old dumps	25
Pyrrhotite tailings (56 per cent pyrrhotite)	3
	100

Lacking a natural cementing material, a weak mixture of cement and classified fill (85, 86) is gaining wide acceptance in those cases where economies more than offset the extra cost involved. In normal operations scraping floors on the top of hydraulic fill consist of a three inch thickness of 1:6 cement and sand. With say 1:25 cement-tailings fill, the mix can be readily adjusted for this purpose.

The merit of a consolidating fill is not so much in an ability to control wall closure better than other fill as in the advantages of mining to a cohesive fill in pillar recovery, breaking through to filled stopes from below and in the added stability of such fill in wide stopes, figures 69 and 70.

Here the experience at the Geco Division of Noranda Mines Limited is of interest. The orebody, varying in width up to 100 feet and with a near vertical dip, was being mined by a long hole sub-level method with transverse stopes. Due to early pillar failures the method was modified to permit supporting the pillars separating stopes over most of the mining cycle. Stopes were field blasted with a substantial choke effect, after which a coarse quarried fill was run in on top of the broken ore. As the ore was drawn down the coarse fill followed, maintaining a well-defined interface while also supporting the walls.

It was later found that by introducing classified cemented tailings into the voids of the coarse fill it was possible to mine directly alongside, with no fencing and no serious disturbance of the fill (87).

Waste filling in the wider and more extensive orebodies should never be totally dependent on pillar support for stability. There are cases where the failure of such a pillar system has resulted in general subsidence, including fill, pillars, and levels through them, over the vertical extent of the pillar-supported area. Consolidated fill gives some protection against this possibility.

UNIT-TYPE SUPPORTS

The stability of a mine can be ensured by pillar support, by filling methods or by a controlled caving operation. Regardless of the method used the security of

FIGURE 69 Mining of a pillar is proceeding directly alongside a stope which was mined by the cut-and-fill method and filled with cemented sand. The height of the stabilized fill is approximately 20 feet, as indicated by the loading stick held by the miner. The additional strength of the fill allows the pillar to be mined by the more economical cut-and-fill method, as well as eliminating the necessity of a timber fence. (*Courtesy of INCO*)

FIGURE 70 In this undercut-and-fill pillar the use of cemented sand fill has made it possible to replace laminated stringers and a solid log mat with a much simpler and less expensive screen-type mat supported on stringers. (*Courtesy of INCO*)

working faces, access ways, and unsupported spans must be provided for. This is accomplished by the use of various forms of support referred to as unit types as they consist of individual members the effectiveness of which is limited to stoping widths (heights) generally less than about ten feet and to local or unit areas of the mine.

In some cases a degree of rigidity is desirable; in other cases the support must be of a compressible nature and occasionally a time factor is the ruling element in the choice. Practice is naturally dominated by local material costs and wage rates and extremes in practice are often the result.

Over the mining range the use of unit types of support is so widespread that experience is necessary to develop a perspective on their application. However, as their purpose is safe operating conditions with regard to time factors, rigidity, and compressibility, the following types represent the range usually available in stoping.

Stulls, Posts and Props — A large support timber, hanging to footwall in inclined deposits, is referred to as a stull; smaller ones are called spraggs. In flatter deposits a similar timber, roof to floor, is referred to as a post or prop. For convenience in handling they are usually limited to lengths of about ten feet, though if mine openings permit this length can be exceeded when desired. They represent a traditional type of support, in many cases now superseded by rockbolts and / or steel friction or hydraulic props.

For all practical purposes the timber stull or post is rigid up to the point of failure. With the development of failure conditions its usefulness can be extended by the additions of a head board or squeeze block. This is a piece of soft wood inserted at the hangingwall to take pressure across the grain. In spite of numerous substitutes the timber stull still finds a place in most operations, figure 50. Powered supports (88, 89) are a recent development of composite units, each consisting of several hydraulic props, which can be advanced as a unit. The initial cost per foot of longwall face is perhaps twice that for individual props, but they are designed to improve productivity and thus to reduce face costs.

Rockbolts — There are various types and sizes. The anchoring device at the end of the bolt may be a wedged slot or, more commonly, a four-pronged shell. The latter is tightened by a torque wrench against a bearing plate at the rock face to any desired tension. The turning action draws a tapered nut into the pronged shell. which is thus expanded to give a firm friction grip on the surface of the hole. With either type of anchorage a grip exceeding the strength of the bolt is possible. When justified economically, filling the space around the bolt with resin also improves the bonding.

Bolts installed close to a working face tend to lose tension in some cases, perhaps due to defective seating of collar plates. This is usually overcome by retightening on one or more occasions as the face advances.

The rockbolt, five feet or more in length, with or without wire mesh netting, has practically displaced the stull and timber set as a supporting unit, figures 71,

FIGURE 71 A main air transfer drift[109]

72, and 73. In doing so it has facilitated the use of mechanical equipment by the elimination of timber obstructions, and has improved safety, and reduced dilution. Some shrinkage stoping operations have been carried beyond their normal range by the pattern bolting of the walls in the course of mining. The rockbolt has a reinforcing characteristic, but this should not be overemphasized because with sufficient pressure, failure conditions will develop in spite of the best bolting practice.

Various modifications have developed in bolting practice. There is a trend towards the use of steel reinforcing bars as used in concrete, and fiber glass pins and bolts, grouting them in place with either cement or a self-hardening plastic. The use of rock anchors and cable bolting also appears to be increasing.

The effectiveness of the rockbolt depends upon the anchorage. When the fracture zone extends beyond the anchorage, conditions are less positive and large falls of ground containing numerous rockbolts are not uncommon. Theory is occa-

FIGURE 72 Screenbolting in a wide intersection. (*Courtesy of INCO*)

sionally introduced to determine safe operating spans, but when safety is a primary consideration, until we can predict the outline of a fracture zone we must depend upon trial and error methods for the answer.

In the meantime, in any underground excavation, within limited spans, the rockbolt can be accepted as one of the most useful types of support, but it cannot be expected to hold a sagging hangingwall in place over indefinite spans. It has a place in the control of fracture zone development in stopes and its use is acceptable only when the anchorage is in unruptured rock.

Cribsets — In narrow stoping, with the failure of stulls and head boards under a sagging hangingwall, a more compressible support is indicated. On any dip the cribset or pig stye partially fills this role. It has the advantage that under pressure it tightens, but its four points of contact offer very little initial resistance to converging walls. This was countered to some extent by filling the crib with waste rock, but even so there is very little early resistance. However, well-built cribsets under pressure remain in place offering increasing resistance to wall closure on any dip. Similar to most timber supports the cribset obstructs a working place and on flat dips may result in some limitations in the use of mechanical equipment, figure 74.

FIGURE 73 Rock bolts and welded mesh screen supporting the back in a cut and fill stope. (*Courtesy of INCO*)

Mat Packs — These are a development from the cribset and are extensively used on the Witwatersrand where the stoping width averages only about four feet. They are eighteen inches and upwards square and for convenience in handling are assembled as units, figure 75. The units consist of a course of four-inch round timber sawn parallel on two sides, cut to length, and bolted together to form a mat. The mats can then be built into a solid timber support with pressure acting across the grain. Thus while fulfilling a similar function they offer more effective early resistance than filled cribsets.

Waste Walls — In flat open stopes with waste broken with the ore, wage rates permitting, it is natural to think of building waste walls, supporting the hangingwall, and improving the grade at the same time. These walls developed with the flat dips of coal mining practice and a limited application is found also on the steeper dips of metal mines. Their primary purpose is to reduce wall closure and control the hangingwall and footwall in the process, figures 76 and 77.

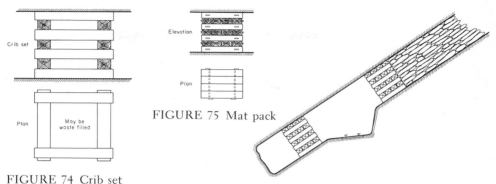

Crib set

Plan   May be waste filled

FIGURE 74 Crib set

Elevation

Plan

FIGURE 75 Mat pack

FIGURE 76 Dry waste wall and mat packs

In the deep, steeply dipping lodes of the Kolar gold field in India with an average width of about five feet, filled cribsets were supplemented by walls of granite blocks with two parallel faces, figure 77. The reduction of fire risk, low wage rates, and high cost of timber were all factors in adopting the system, which was primarily aimed at arresting the closure of stope walls. Such walls did improve support, but

FIGURE 77 Dry granite walling (filled crib in foreground), Kolar Gold Field, South India

under pressure, even when built with cement mortar, they did not significantly arrest closure of stope walls or prevent rockbursts. Like many unit types of support the attractiveness of waste rock walling will vary inversely with wage rates involved.

Square-Setting — This is a type of timber support built up of individual units. It was first developed by Philip Deidesheimer about 1860 at the Ophir mine on the Comstock lode in Nevada to mine a high grade deposit of very friable ore somewhat too wide to mine by any conventional method then known.

In the process of experimenting with timber support a square-set method was developed which was the forerunner of the various methods in use today. With this somewhat crude method an opening several hundred feet in length, 60 to 100 feet wide, and 400 feet high was mined and supported.

The conventional square-set unit consists of four posts, two caps, and two girts framed to fit together as a unit. A round of sufficient depth and height is blasted to permit the insertion of one or more such units, which are then blocked by wedging to the walls and back, figure 78.

Square-setting in large open stopes has limitations as regards stability of the sets and for this reason the practice finds its most general application in longitudinal or transverse stopes with widths limited to about 35 feet when combined with filling. As such it is perhaps the highest cost mining method and in many cases is a last resort when other methods have failed. It must now compete with rockbolts and wire mesh netting and also with underhand and fill methods now well developed with and without the use of cement.

Support in Shafts

The function of support in shafts is to control sloughing of the walls, to permit and maintain the alignment of guides or track, to carry pipes and cables, to provide manway, service and hoisting compartments, and generally to ensure safe hoisting and service facilities upon which the continuous operation of the mine depends.

When pronounced schistosity or bedding planes are parallel or nearly so to the direction of the shaft, ground control is simplified if the major axis of the shaft is normal to such planes. This facility is more readily provided for vertical than for inclined shafts.

From earlier references to stress distributions and to stress zones, it is apparent that shafts should be located to avoid the extremes in stress distribution resulting from stoping.

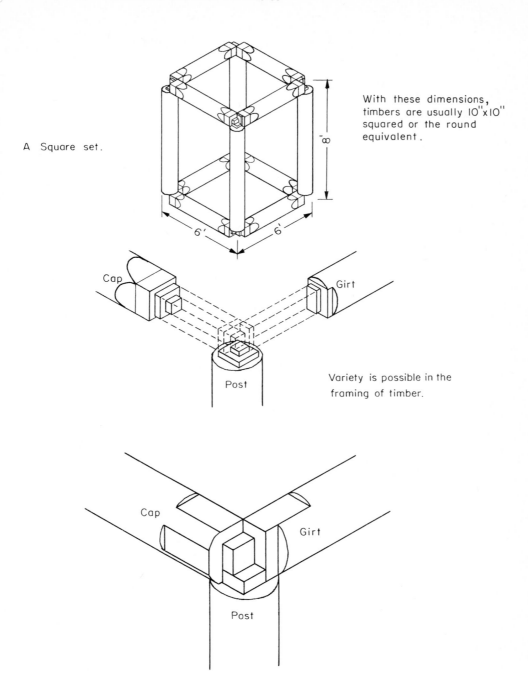

A Square set.

With these dimensions, timbers are usually 10"x10" squared or the round equivalent.

8'

6'   6'

Cap

Girt

Post

Variety is possible in the framing of timber.

Cap

Girt

Post

FIGURE 78 A square set and joint details

Vertical shafts, and inclined shafts steeper than the angle of repose, are usually supported throughout their entire length. Below the angle of repose, in good ground inclined shafts require only footwall backing pieces to carry the roads and ladderway, and occasionally hangingwall plates or rockbolts to carry pipes and cables. In poorer ground conventional shaft sets are required. The discussion which follows refers specifically to vertical shafts, but if one bears in mind distinctions which must arise with dips less than vertical, the case of steeply dipping inclines is very similar.

In Canada, long rectangular shafts of three or more compartments, and square types, figure 79, have been favoured. Such shafts lend themselves to either steel or to timber sets consisting of wall plates, end plates, posts, and dividers. The framing of timber shaft sets, along with square sets and level sets, is part of the timberman's craft and will vary in detail on different operations. Shaft sets vary from 8-inch by 8-inch to 10-inch by 10-inch timbers. Bearing sets may be of either timber or steel. A lining behind the sets, as a protection against loose, is commonly of two-inch plank though other forms of sheeting have been used.

Bearing sets are hitched into the walls below the collar across the short dimension of the shaft. The collar timbering is built up from these bearers in many cases inside a concrete collar. Sets below the bearers are suspended by hanging irons from set to set from the bearers down and are lined, blocked, and wedged as placed. Bearing sets are placed below each station and at intermediate points as required.

With depth, the requirements of ventilation and ground pressure are more rigorous and alternatives to timber-supported shafts are favoured. These are the circular or elliptical shafts lined with concrete or bricks, figure 79. The elliptical shape is preferable when its outline conforms with the natural arching of the ground.

In these shafts timber may be used to carry guides and equipment but steel is perhaps more common. In fields using steel buntons to carry equipment, it is common practice to have the runners or guides of steel also. This precludes the usual safety dogs on cages and throws more emphasis on rope inspection.

In exceptionally good ground, circular vertical shafts have been sunk and operated to substantial depth with no support whatever. They are equipped with rope guides hung from the head frame and weighted at the bottom. They are hoisting shafts only without manways or service facilities, but are also good ventilation openings.

Support in Levels

Support in levels involves a wide variety of problems, but the principle of either rigid or compressible support is always present. Levels in the solid in good ground normally require little or no support even at considerable depth, but through stoping areas and in their vicinity ground conditions involving a supporting problem are likely to arise.

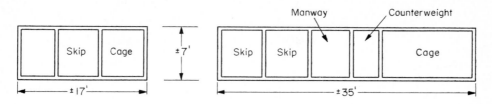

Long Rectangular Types

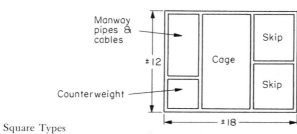

Square Types

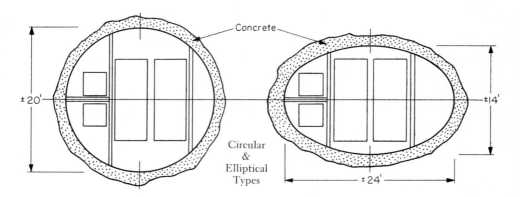

Circular
&
Elliptical
Types

FIGURE 79 Shaft sections

Level maintenance costs or their alternative in the form of footwall access drifts have been largely responsible for the development of retreating methods of mining. With these methods a stoping sequence is planned which permits access to the stopes through levels in the solid. As the stoping progresses the level through the stoped area can be abandoned. Alternatively, advancing methods usually depend upon the maintenance of levels through stoped ground.

The choice of either method is a matter of costs. Establishing retreating facilities involves an early concentration of development costs and the deferment of production by the time factor involved in this initial work. In return, the maintenance of levels over the life of the operation is greatly reduced as compared with an advancing method.

The support of levels through stoping areas depends primarily on the support in the stopes. Through narrow open stope areas with no pillar support, wall closure will be reflected on levels and in extreme cases the level width may be critically reduced. There is no level-supporting alternative to this problem beyond slashing the level to an adequate width. Alternatively, the level may be abandoned in favour of footwall access. A similar situation arises in narrow filled stopes in the absence of crown and sill pillars when the stope width is such that the compression on the fill can seriously reduce the level width. In this case it will be appreciated that the compression of the fill is a function of the stoping span rather than of the stoping width.

At some stage in the stress progression, levels through sill and crown pillars giving access to filled or open stopes become costly if not dangerous to maintain. If the sills and crowns fail there is also the problem in wide filled stopes of the stability of the fill.

With little ground pressure for level support through rock openings, the operator has the choice of the more rigid methods. The conventional timber set, figure 80, has been the traditional method and still has a place in the problem, but rigidity and newer alternatives limit its range of usefulness.

Gunite, and more recently, shotcrete with its coarser aggregate, along with conventional concrete, brick, and masonry level linings all have a place in the supporting picture, but with increasing ground pressure the usefulness of concrete is limited by its rigidity to the range of competence in compression and / or shear, figure 81.

The most common level support at the present time is the rockbolt. By itself or in conjunction with strapping plates, wire mesh screening, and / or gunite it has an application limited only by exceptionally heavy ground or extremes in pressure, figures 71, 72, and 73.

Under extreme ground pressure no supporting material is likely to provide the rigidity required to arrest ground movement. With the development of ground pressure in levels there is thus no alternative to support of a compressible nature. Within this context steel level sets of different types have proved very effective, figures 82, 83, and 84. Under pressure conditions they may be deformed but in the process offer continuous resistance.

FIGURE 80 Timber drift sets[109]

FIGURE 81 A concreted slusher drift[109]

FIGURE 82 Yielding arch sets installed in a slusher drift[109]

The yielding steel arch, figure 82, has had a wide application. This, varying through horseshoe to circular form, consists of two or more members of similar sections, 18 to 24 pounds per foot, held together by bolted clamps. They adjust to pressure by a sliding action controlled by the friction of section on section resulting from the tightness of the clamps. These sets are designed for quite high resistance

FIGURE 83 Steel sets – 4″ × 4″ – section Kolar Gold Field, South India

FIGURE 84 Steel drift sets with rock bolted and screened walls[109]

and are efficient when the loading conforms with the design. Too frequently in practice this is not the case and sets designed to deform with less resistance under any loading may be more effective, figure 83.

The efficiency of most compressible supports is related to a time factor associated with the ground movement. Under this condition suitably designed steel sets, with few exceptions, are likely to be more effective than other forms of support. This is particularly true when a rockburst risk is present.

In narrow steeply dipping orebodies at depth there is frequently a tendency for the floor to heave and the back to arch with the approach of stoping. Under certain economic conditions practice has trended towards placing supports below the floor and over the back as part of the initial stope preparation.

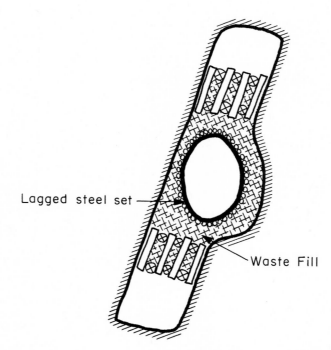

Lagged steel set

Waste Fill

FIGURE 85 Stope preparation and level setting, Kolar Gold Field, South India

The case is illustrated in figure 85. The floor is mined to a depth permitting the installation of cribsets. These are filled with waste and covered with lagging on which waste is also placed to carry the track. The back is also taken down to a sufficient height to install cribsets which are lagged over for protection. The walls may be bolted, but if rockbursts are a problem the level may also be supported with steel sets. With such an arrangement stopes can commence at or break through to the level from above or below with the level effectively protected.

For flatter dips where it is also desirable to maintain the hangingwall intact a similar practice, usually with bolting, has developed both in coal mining and in narrow stope metal mines, figure 76.

Summary and Conclusions

The principles underlying ground control are very simple. During mining, the rock mass surrounding the mining excavation must be retained rigidly in place or it must be induced to rupture under a high degree of control. These principles are illustrated respectively in rigid pillar and longwall mining methods. Increasing ground pressure usually forces a transition from the former to the latter.

The effect of the earliest mining in an orebody, upon the cost and final recovery for the orebody as a whole, is a primary ground control consideration.

In general, the fundamental distinction in ground control is that between the use of pillar supported mining methods and the use of a longwall sequence which eliminates the need for pillars. In a rockburst context the longwall sequence is essential in reducing rockburst incidence. In the absence of rockbursts pillar-supported methods may be carried into the range of progressive ground failure but usually there is a break-even point with longwall sequential mining based upon lost ore and increasing operating costs. Locating such a point is still a matter for judgement.

The proportion of fatalities due to falls of ground focuses attention on unit type supports for the control of loose. On the other hand the successful application of most mining methods depends upon general mine stability which is achieved by mass support in the form of rigid pillars, or filling, or by predictable caving methods of mining.

The use of rigid or compressible support is dictated by pressure conditions and the trend with depth is towards compressibility for both mass and unit type supports.

Pillars can be justified as support only so long as their loading can be maintained within safe limits or gradual failure on a time basis can be predicted. With increasing pressure rigid pillars as support give way to longwall principles and the introduction of fill. A better control is possible with a naturally consolidating fill but this usually depends upon the local availability of such materials. Failing this, a weak cement sand mixture has gained wide acceptance where conditions justify the extra cost.

Experience is essential to develop a perspective on the application of unit type supports. Even so there are many cases where the most suitable alternative must be determined through a process of on site trial and error.

4 | The Operating Spectrum

The Background

The incentive behind most mining activities has been the hope of profit and over the years the technology and economics of the times have determined the demarcation line between ore and waste. At any particular time both technology and economics are dependent on basic scientific knowledge and the facilities to be derived therefrom. As scientific knowledge expands, new developments follow. In present day mining such developments have been related to the application of energy in its various forms: appropriate mechanical design and improved material properties. A short review will indicate historical trends.

EXPLOSIVES

Prior to the use of explosives the world's mining was confined largely to placer and detrital deposits and to good-grade ore structures of comparatively narrow width. Output was limited by the capacity of wind, water, hand, and animal power. Agricola's (90) description of such a world is of historical interest today.

Black powder was widely known in the thirteenth century and came into military use during the fourteenth century. Its use in mines is first recorded in Germany shortly before 1627, in the lead mines of Derbyshire in 1670, and in the Cornish tin mines in 1689.

Sobrero, a chemistry professor in Turin, discovered nitroglycerine in 1847. There were great risks involved in handling this very sensitive liquid. After much experimenting, Nobel in 1866 produced dynamite no. 1 by absorbing nitroglycerine in Kieselguhr in the proportions 3 to 1 by weight. This development, together with the blasting cap of fulminate of mercury, also due to Nobel, added much to the safety and positiveness of nitroglycerine for practical use. Further developments resulted in a variety of specialized dynamites, gelatines, ammonia nitrate types of explosives, and detonating facilities which improved safety and removed all but economic limitations on the breaking of rock.

Ammonium nitrate has been an ingredient of certain types of explosives for many years. It was cheap, supplied oxygen, and lowered the temperature of explosion but was regarded as an explosive base only when coated with a high explosive, such as nitroglycerine. After a few catastrophic explosions — Opau, Galveston — it was found in the 1950s that when mixed with suitable combustibles, with liquid hydro-carbons preferred on a cost basis, it was no longer insensitive to detonation and became an explosive base in its own right. As a result of this development and continuing research, ammonium nitrate mixed in suitable proportions with fuel oil or, for open pit work, as a slurry with TNT and / or aluminum powder with or without $NaNO_3$, has now replaced the older conventional explosives for most mining purposes.

Explosives Formulae —

Black Powder = $20KNO_3 + 30C + 10S$
$$\longrightarrow 6K_2CO_3 + K_2SO_4 + 3K_2S_3 + 14CO_2 + 10N_2 + 10CO$$
Glycerin = $C_3H_5(OH)_3$; nitration; Nitroglycerin = $C_3H_5(ONO_2)_3$
$$4C_3H_5(ONO_2)_3 \longrightarrow 12CO_2 + 10H_2O + 6N_2 + O_2$$
Glycol = $C_2H_4(OH)_2$; nitration; Dinitroglycol =
Ethylene Glycol Dinitrate = $C_2H_4(ONO_2)_2$
= low freezing ingredient
Nitro-cellulose = Gun Cotton = $C_6H_7O_5(NO_2)_3$
Trinitrotoluene = TNT = $C_7H_5(NO_2)_3$
$$2C_7H_5(NO_2)_3 \longrightarrow 12CO + 2CH_4 + 3N_2 + H_2$$
Ammonium Nitrate = NH_4NO_3 Fuel Oil = CH_2
    mix ratio by weight   94.5%   5.5%
$$3NH_4NO_3 + CH_2 \longrightarrow 3N_2 + 7H_2O + CO_2$$

ROCK DRILLING

When black powder was originally applied to mining it was, no doubt, used in cracks and fissures until the idea of drilling holes in the rock emerged. This inspired experimental work in rock drilling which still continues. When dynamite first became available, drilling technique had progressed as far as hand work and the steel of the day permitted. Shortly after this the compressed-air operated percussion drill was developed, and with improving design this type of equipment gradually superseded the hand driller.

During the 1930s competitive costs in most areas permitted the detachable bit to displace conventional steel rods. With extension rods and alloy or carbon steel bits, percussion drill holes up to 20 feet in length became economical in special cases. Beyond this length costs favoured the diamond drill, and in either case were outside the accepted economical range for stoping.

Under these conditions the diamond drill existed as an exploration tool. Costs were high as practice demanded that bits be set with a few large stones at a cost ranging up to $2000 for even the smaller bits. During the 1930s these large stones were successfully displaced by fines and poorer grade small stones at a great reduction in price. For low cost breaking in stopes the longer hole was an ideal, and with the lowered diamond cost such holes now become available within the stoping cost range. The result was the initiation of diamond drill blast hole or long hole sublevel stoping.

During World War II, the tungsten carbide bit was developed in both Germany and Sweden. This bit in some cases improved drilling speed, but its major contribution was an ability to resist abrasion. Costs were reduced and loss of gauge was no longer a limiting factor in the economical drilling of long holes. On a cost basis the tungsten carbide bit soon displaced bits of carbon or alloy steel. It also put the percussion drill in competition with the diamond drill for long stoping holes. With few exceptions the cost pattern now favours the percussion drill for such work.

With hand drilling, the optimum depth of hole was about four feet and mining practice was oriented around this dimension. Extending the depth of hole to about 10 feet by machine drilling, with alloy and carbon steel, had only a minor effect on the evolution of mining practice. Conversely, the optimum depth of hole now possible with tungsten-carbide bits has not yet been fully exploited.

The economical drilling of large holes is a rapidly improving technique, and the boring of 48-inch and larger holes now competes with conventional raising in hard rock.

MECHANICAL POWER

Until the age of steam the world's work had been accomplished by water wheels, windmills, and animal and human power. The depth of mining was limited by this type of power and some of the early applications of steam were directed towards the improvement of mine hoisting and pumping facilities. The man engine and Cornish pump, both ingenious devices in their day, have long since become museum pieces.

Steam power for hoisting was confined to surface installations and hoisting depth was originally limited by the strength of vegetable fibre ropes. Iron wire ropes appear to have been used consistently for mining in Germany from about 1834. With the development of steel, improvement in the quality of material and manufacturing have given us the very efficient steel wire ropes of today.

The depth to which single stage hoisting can proceed depends upon the quality of the rope and the factor of safety demanded. For many years an optimum economic depth for single stage hoisting of about 4500 feet had been generally accepted in the mining world. However, it was recognized that long ropes require a lower factor of safety with the result that single lifts up to 8000 feet can now be contemplated.

The use of electric power in mines was very limited fifty years ago. Under this condition compressed air was the chief source of underground power. Today, with the exception of percussion drilling and some service facilities (chutes), most underground and surface mining operations depend directly upon electrical energy generated by steam, water, or diesel power.

With the facilities presently at our disposal, it is safe to say that the depth to which mining can proceed is a matter of costs rather than technology and is thus limited only by the demand for the mineral involved.

Looking to the future there is no doubt that the trend towards lower costs and greater tonnages will continue. The recent shifts in rock drilling and explosive practices are only indications of the rapidity of change. Great progress is also apparent in materials handling over a wide range. The hydraulic transport of solids is making rapid strides. Improved design in earth-moving equipment removes earlier limitations on both open pit and underground practice. Multirope suspension has greatly expanded the application of friction hoists. Computers and complicated mechanical and electrical control gear are becoming commonplace.

The mechanization of mines has reached a point where there is little place for unskilled labour. The average mine employee requires a capital outlay for equipment and facilities varying from about $25,000 upwards before he is effectively at work. The miner at the working face is a skilled craftsman requiring the services of numerous other craftsmen to maintain the equipment he requires. The trend is towards push-button operations requiring wider and greater skills, an example being in the use of powered supports. The possibilities of atomic energy are still ahead of us for such applications as the leaching of metals and tar sand types of deposits.

ECONOMIC FACTORS

With costs and thus grade of ore rather than technology limiting the scope of mining operations, the maximum profit, consistent with safety, becomes the criterion in the selection of a mining method.

Selective methods are usually designed for a high mining recovery, while mass production methods accept the possibility of the loss of a proportion of the ore in pillars and through dilution. Thus, in estimating the overall cost, the proportion of the orebody likely to be recovered is an important factor. It is obvious that the higher the grade of the ore the less desirable are methods which are likely to involve loss of ore.

The point is illustrated in figure 86 which gives a comparison between a mass production method, involving the risk of ore losses and dilution but costing

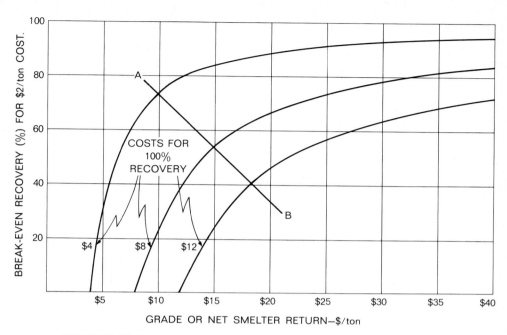

FIGURE 86 Recoveries for a method costing $2/ton to break-even with 100% recovery by methods costing $4, $8 and $12/ton respectively

only $2 / ton, and more selective methods estimated to recover 100 per cent of the ore at costs of $4 / ton, $8 / ton, and $12 / ton respectively.* Break-even points for the $2 / ton method are shown for varying grades against the curves for the 100 per cent recovery methods.

It will be noted on the graph, for a grade of $15 / ton, that if the $2 / ton method recovers only 23 per cent of the ore it breaks even with 100 per cent recovery by the $12 / ton method. On the other hand, in competition with the $4 / ton method, the $2 / ton method must recover 84 per cent of the ore to break even.

This emphasizes that with increasing grades, the trend above the line A — B is towards high cost selectivity in the choice of methods. Below the line with decreasing grades, the ore losses associated with the lower cost mass production methods become more and more acceptable.

Good mining practice is a search within the range of safety for the maximum profit. Alternatives are always in competition and break-even points determine priorities. These occasionally lend themselves to direct analysis, but more often the

*All monetary values used in the text are for illustrative purposes only.

range of variables present places a greater premium on good judgement than in most other industries.

Surface Mining

OPEN PIT OPERATIONS

The terminology applies to any mining operation carried out under surface conditions. It ranges from conventional open pits and quarries through strip mining of coal and other minerals to various types of earth and gravel excavations, including some types of placer mining, but excluding placer dredging operations. Economic factors limit the operation laterally and in depth.

This method of mining is particularly applicable with deposits of substantial tonnage per vertical foot, on any dip. Some open pits are operated on material too low in value to permit underground mining. More often their operation depends upon showing a greater profit than is possible by underground methods. The break-even point between open pit and underground mining costs thus represents an economic limit for open pit operations. This point, or an ore value which is lower, limits the amount of waste which can be removed in maintaining pit walls and access ways at slopes which are both safe and economical.

The layout of an open pit depends upon relating ground conditions to economic factors. A contoured map of the surface and sufficient sampling data to establish ore outlines to the desired depth are essential. These, together with an estimated slope for pit walls and a waste / ore cut-off ratio, permit estimating payable limits both laterally and in depth.

The slope of pit walls is a major factor in open pit design. Too steep a slope carries undesirable risks, but a slope less than required for safety can involve millions of dollars in extra waste removal. It also advances the break-even point for underground mining.

When the cohesion and the angle of internal friction, as obtained in laboratory tests, can be applied to ground *in situ*, the principles of soil mechanics apply and acceptable estimates of ground slopes may be possible. As these values increase their application to ground *in situ* is less reliable and empiricism related to local conditions takes precedence in establishing the slope of pit walls. For this condition, which is general over the hard rock range, slopes vary with local conditions and with few exceptions range between 40° and 60° with the horizontal. When hydraulic effects are involved, slopes are lower.

Given the slope for pit walls, individual cross-sections are compiled at suitable intervals, 50 to 100 feet being common, and cut-off lines are calculated. The relevant data from such cross-sections is then assembled on plans and longitudinal sections and with due allowance for roadways in waste and slopes at the pit ends, benches can be established within payable limits.

A maximum bench height of 65 feet is prescribed in some mining regulations. There are risks as well as economies in high benches. Rock properties, structural features, drilling practice, and scaling requirements all influence the decision.

A computer can eliminate much of the repetitive work related to grade, costs, and mining limits in open pit design but results can be only as reliable as the data supplied. An over-simplified aspect of the economics of open pit design is illustrated in the following example. This is limited to the analyses of cross-sections assuming a horizontal surface and also that the pit is long enough to disregard the slope of pit ends and road work outside of payable limits, figure 87.

Example:

OREBODY

Width	A maximum of 250 feet is shown in figure 87.
Length	Great as compared with width, to permit disregarding slope conditions at the pit ends.
Depth	Open, but assured by drilling over the desired range.

OPERATING COSTS

Open Pit	$0.40 / ton for both ore and waste.
Underground	$1.20 / ton for ore.

CAPITAL COSTS

Open Pit	$1500 / daily ton of ore.
Underground	$4000 / daily ton of ore.
Plant	Common to both pit and underground.

SLOPE OF PIT WALLS   55°

TONNAGE FACTOR   10 c.f. / ton, ore and waste.

The cost and slope data, representing estimates only, permit a strong element of judgement in final conclusions.

Figure 88 represents a cross-section through the orebody. With open pit operating costs at $0.40 / ton and underground at $1.20 / ton, disregarding capital costs for the time being, two tons of waste can be mined with each ton of ore before open pit operating costs approach those for underground work. This establishes a marginal waste / ore cut-off ratio of 2:1.

Assuming the surface is approximately horizontal, the pit can be deepened with walls sloped at 55° until mining requires the removal of two tons of waste for each ton of ore made available.

$2W = 2D \cos 55°$; $H / D = \sin 55°$ & $D = H / \sin 55°$

Thus $H = 1.43W = 286'$ & $D = 349'$

From the above, this cut-off point is obtained at a depth of 1.43 times the width of ore made available. The cut-off ratio of 2:1 also establishes an average mining

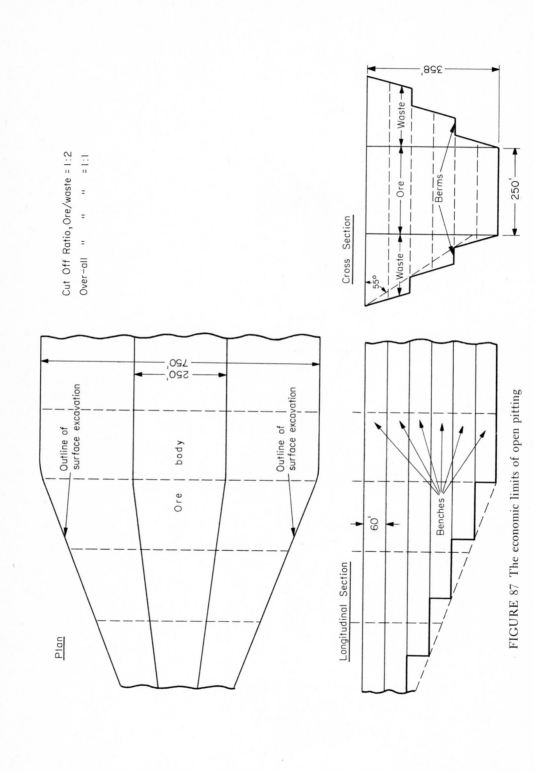

Cut Off Ratio, Ore/waste = 1:2
Over-all   "   "   "   = 1:1

Plan

Outline of
surface excavation

Ore   body

Ore

Outline of
surface excavation

750'

250'

Cross   Section

358'

250'

55°

Waste

Ore

Waste

Waste

Berms

Longitudinal   Section

60'

Benches

FIGURE 87 The economic limits of open pitting

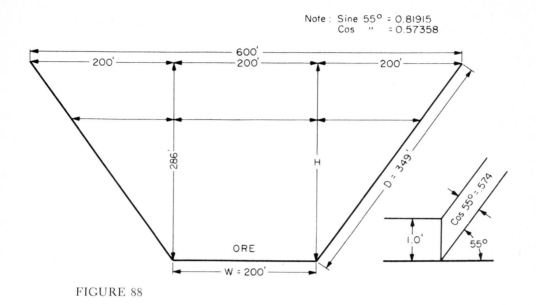

FIGURE 88

ratio, waste / ore, of 1:1, if the possibility of further deepening in ore is disregarded. This ratio normally is independent of the slope of pit walls. The latter, however, determines the depth of the open pit and thus the total tonnage available.

Open pit average cost is thus $2 \times \$0.40 = \$0.80$ / ton of ore for this section. This indicates an open pit profit over that for underground mining of $\$1.20 - \$0.80 = \$0.40$ / ton from which, for the pit as a whole, capital must be provided. This greatly oversimplified comparison of open pit and underground mining has an application with any orebody, the extent and grade of which permits underground mining. When through grade or other causes there is no alternative to open pit operations, operating costs and recoverable grade determine cut-off and overall waste / ore ratios. With varying surface contours and ore widths the calculation is more complicated.

A series of cross-sections at suitable intervals permits outlining the projected pit excavation in both plan and longitudinal section as shown in figure 87. Assuming bench heights of 60 feet, benches can be fitted within the payable limits. With the pit bottom and benches thus established a more accurate calculation of the overall waste / ore ratio upon which cost per ton of ore depends is possible.

Assuming this ratio is 0.9 tons of waste per ton of ore, then the average open pit costs are $0.9 \times \$0.40 + \$0.40 = \$0.76$ / ton. This subtracted from the underground cost of $1.20 leaves an operating profit of $0.44 / ton of ore in favour of the open pit.

The daily output to be established demands a consideration of the time value of money both as to operating and capital costs. On this basis ore reserves must be adequate to write off the estimated capital cost of $1500 / daily ton and leave a surplus sufficient to provide a profit over and above possible errors in the estimates.

PLATE A An 8 cubic yard shovel loading an 85 ton truck—Copper Mountain Open Pit. Note jointing in the pit walls. (Courtesy of Gaspe Copper Mines Limited)

The above principles indicate the basic economic factors involved in determining the feasibility of open pit operations for any orebody or of the strip mining for coal over the range in dip from horizontal to vertical. Obviously there is a limiting thickness or width of ore below which open pit operations cease to be attractive.

In operating an open pit with vertical drilling patterns, due to overbreak bench faces usually slough back to about 70° from the horizontal. Some recent practice is towards inclined holes to give better breaking facilities and safer slopes with less sub-grade drilling.

As the pit is deepened, in the process of maintaining pit slopes it is usual to leave a portion of some benches projecting horizontally into the pit as a protection against falling rock. These projections are termed berms and to get greater width within the overall slope they are occasionally established at alternate benches.

Access to the pit is again a matter of economics. Rail haulage can be cheap, but for pits deepened from surface the 2 1/2 per cent maximum grade usually permitted extends the haulage distance and in many cases involves a prohibitive amount of waste removal. The 8 to 10 per cent grade available with truck haulage is much more favourable. Truck haulage roads at these grades can be spiralled or switch-backed down the pit as it deepens. As depth increases, however, truck haulage is in competition with skip hoisting from the pit bottom. In the latter case ore is hauled by truck on the pit floor to a crusher and / or a skip loading pocket from where it is hoisted in heavy skips to surface.

Open pit equipment follows the conventional pattern in drilling equipment, power shovels, heavy trucks, and bulldozers, the performance of which is continuously being improved. Illustrations of such equipment are plentiful in the technical journals. Here it is sufficient to note that consistent with the order of magnitude of the tonnage involved, the lowest costs will follow the heaviest equipment.

In concluding, reference should be made to some of the imponderables which modify cut-off points and ore / waste ratios determined from cost estimates only. Cases will arise, as for instance in asbestos mining, where any sorting of waste, which may be considerable, is economically impossible with an underground operation but quite effective in an open pit. Also the possibility that the extra handling involved in underground operations degrades the product somewhat may be a factor. Considerations such as these cannot always be expressed in absolute values and open pit operations may thus be justified beyond conventional cut-off points.

Underground Mining

DEVELOPMENT

With or without geophysical assistance an orebody is usually indicated by surface trenching or drilling of one type or another. If this work is sufficiently encouraging as regards tonnage and grade the next step is the provision of facilities for open pit or underground operations.

The original underground work has the immediate objective of confirming the dimensions, grade, and structure of the orebody as precisely as possible to a depth sufficient to meet initial production requirements. The openings required are a shaft (or an adit in mountainous country) from which levels connected by raises are driven at suitable intervals to cover the depth required. It is usual, after diamond drilling, to design and locate the shaft and space the levels in a manner most appropriate for their use over the exploration, development, and production phases.

Shafts — Figure 79 shows sections of various types of shafts. With the three-compartment shaft, two compartments may be reserved for balanced hoisting while the third compartment carries a ladderway along with pipes and cables. For hoisting it is usual to have a cage slung below the skip or vice versa in one or both roads. Shafts of this type are usually adequate for a production rate of about 1000 tons per day from shrinkage stopes.

In the five-compartment shaft there are two skip roads with balanced skips. There is usually provision for one large cage and counterweight — or in exceptional cases with high tonnage, low output per working place, and the additional servicing required — two large cages in balance. Manway, service pipes, and cables occupy the remaining space.

Circular shafts, due to advantages in ventilation and in ground control, are common both in coal and deep mining practice. An elliptical shape with the long axis across the strike has advantages in ground weakened by steeply dipping schist or bedding planes. The additional length permits a sinking compartment when sinking and production proceed simultaneously. The lining for both circular and elliptical shafts is usually of concrete, but occasionally bricks have an application.

For ore dipping steeper than about 60°, the use of the vertical shaft is almost universal. As the dip flattens, the inclined shaft becomes competitive. The relative merit of the inclined as compared to the vertical shaft is a problem in local economics. In general, for any given size the vertical shaft has a higher output and lower maintenance cost.

The increasing use underground of power shovels, dump trucks, load-haul-dump units, and other heavy trackless equipment has resulted in the "decline": a roadway inclined ± 10°, supplementing shaft facilities in operating and servicing such equipment within the mine. With roadways thus established, jeeps and light trucks can extend servicing facilities and add mobility to supervision in a manner not practicable with conventional shafts only.

A decision on the type of shaft is followed by the problem of location. Here one must consider the cost of cross-cuts to the orebody, travel and tramming distances, and security and the maintenance costs due to the effect of subsequent stoping stresses on the shaft and / or decline and cross-cuts.

The security and maintenance aspect over the projected life of the shaft will depend upon its location with respect to the orebody. The value of early profits is much greater than of those long deferred. However, there is a break-even point between capital outlay today and the cost of long-term security. Maintenance and local conditions frequently demand some compromise with the ideal. Figure 89 represents a few of the options in shaft location.

For steeply dipping lodes of great strike length there is much to be said for location A and the additional cross-cutting and / or mining sequence necessary to avoid a shaft pillar is usually a sound investment. For short strike lengths persisting on a pitch line and also for surface considerations C and E may offer advantages. For extensive orebodies on flat dips location D cannot be avoided and, with present practice, a shaft pillar is essential. As the dip steepens one of the other locations, including the inclined shaft B, becomes competitive. An inclined shaft depending on the mining sequence may or may not require a shaft pillar.

Levels — This term covers the drifts, cross-cuts, and haulages connecting with a shaft station at any particular horizon. They are necessary for both the development and the mining of the orebody. The interval between levels varies with ore distribution and with mining methods and in practice is usually established by experience. However, most mining decisions are based on either safety or costs and the optimum level interval, as a compromise between development and operating requirements is no exception.

If the cost of such openings is to be recovered it is a first charge on the ore developed and mined as a result of them. Thus the greater the interval the lower the development cost per ton (the $1 / X$ ratio, figure 65). On the other hand travel time, service charges to the stope face, and, on occasion, dilution of ore increase with increasing level interval. While the cost refinements necessary to establish any close relationship between dollars and level interval are seldom available at the right time, the relationship involved (based on the following data and the assumption of continuous ore) can be seen in figure 90.

The tonnage factor is 10 c.f. per ton. The ore is assumed to be drift width — 8 feet — and the cost of drifting is $40 / foot. Operating costs are assumed to increase 5 cents per ton (also 10 cents and 20 cents) for every 100 feet of level interval in excess of the first 100 feet. The optimization of level intervals is shown in figure 90.

Raises — These are openings from level to level usually in the plane of the lode. They are required to establish continuity and structure of ore, for ventilation and for stoping facilities. Their number and spacing is a matter of convenience for any particular operation.

Bored raises are now in competition with conventional raising practice. Occasionally such openings are established by sinking rather than raising. In this case they are termed winzes. The term winze is also used to describe an opening approximating a shaft in size which extends the facilities of a surface shaft in depth. These, in effect, are sub-vertical or sub-inclined shafts.

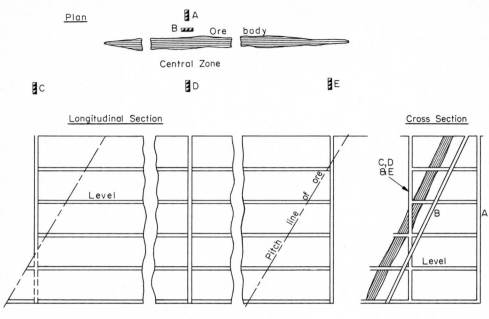

FIGURE 89 Shaft location possibilities

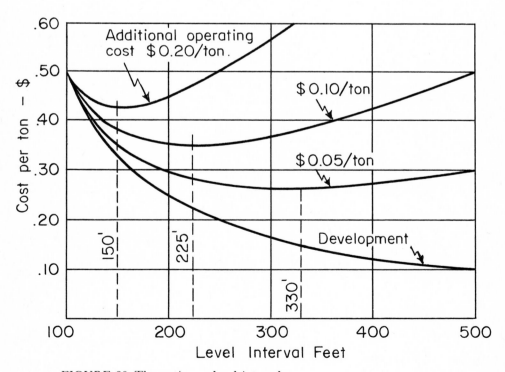

FIGURE 90 The optimum level interval

OPERATING FACILITIES

Some orebodies have clearly defined walls. In others ore limits can be determined only by assay. Orebodies vary in outline from thin tabular deposits of varying lateral and vertical extent, ranging in dip from the vertical to the horizontal, to large compact equidimensional masses. Between these extremes wide variations in rock properties and infinite degrees of irregularity in outline are possible.

The dimensions of orebodies are defined as follows. The length and breadth are, respectively, the major and minor dimensions on the strike-dip plane. The width or thickness is the dimension from hangingwall to footwall or from roof to floor. Similar usage applies with pillars and with longitudinal stopes.

The original development of an orebody is an effort to outline ore limits upon which both reserves and mining facilities will depend. These ore limits with rock properties and stress conditions determine the most appropriate ground control principle. Within the range of this principle some or all of the following operating facilities must be incorporated.

Suitable main arteries from the surface to the orebody in the form of adits, declines or shafts, haulage and travelling ways.

A working face which gives good breaking facilities under safe operating conditions.

Travelling ways between main arteries and the working points for the movement of men and materials, and for services.

Facilities for disposing of broken ore with dilution under control.

Facilities for the introduction of fill or other type of support.

Facilities for disposing of broken waste when desirable.

Facilities for ventilation and drainage.

VARIABLES

The manner in which these facilities are provided will depend upon the variables present in any particular case. Some of the more important are discussed below. The mining method results from the weighting of these variables for ground control and operating facilities.

1. *The Physical Properties of Mine Rocks* — These have been discussed in detail earlier, but the following is pertinent at this point.

In some cases failure conditions in rocks are attributed to the weakness of the rock while in other cases they are attributed to excessive pressure. The distinction is thus relative, but can be expressed as a strength-stress ratio which is an indication of the self-supporting characteristics of the rock or the factor of safety against failure.

The miner, as a result of experience, develops a shrewd sense as to the stability of mine openings under varying conditions and the science of rock mechanics endeavours to express this in quantitative terms.

In the process of deepening a mine, practice has established a gradual trend towards rock failure on the surface of mine openings. Without discounting the possibility of stresses from other sources this does emphasize the importance of the gravitational stress field on mining practice. Methods suitable at shallow depth give way to more rigorous methods as depth increases. In coal mining due to failure in roof, floor, or pillars, longwall supersedes room and pillar practice well short of 2000 feet in vertical depth. In a similar depth range, with steeper dips, harder rocks but greater spans, shrinkage stoping gives way to cut-and-fill to avoid dilution. Also, in all large continuous stoping areas hangingwall sag and footwall heave appear as supporting problems. An empirical factor of safety against failure conditions is an important aspect in determining the most suitable mining dimensions.

2. Length, Breadth, and Width of the Deposit — These dimensions defined above will determine the maximum stope dimensions possible, which in some cases will exceed those desirable for efficient operation. In the narrower ore bodies width is usually a limiting factor in the choice of mining method. With increasing width this limitation disappears to give options in three dimensions. These dimensions also influence decisions as to open or filled stoping, longitudinal or transverse stopes, longwalling on the advance or retreat, caving possibilities and also the most appropriate type of equipment. Up to an optimum the greater the width the more favourable the mining costs are likely to be.

3. The Dip of the Deposit — This will determine the part which gravity may play in the operation. The difference in mining practice between flat and steep dips is one of extremes and the distinction between mining methods is often a matter of the dip of deposits. In the classification which follows, room and pillar methods are reserved for dips below the angle of repose. On steeper dips, where ground control principles vary only in degree, methods associated with sill, crown, and rib pillars have separate classifications.

4. Structural Features of the Rock Mass — Major faults, dikes, contacts, and other pronounced discontinuities representing planes of weakness are factors which should be integrated with ground control. They may influence the location of the initial stopes, the direction of stope faces, the location and orientation of ancillary excavations and also in some cases the distribution of pillars.

5. The Pre-Mining Stress Pattern — The gravitational load increases with depth. Tectonic stresses under the confinement of the gravitational load may show more conspicuous early pressure effects. In either case at some stage in the progression to depth, pillars, projecting remnants, and structural weaknesses as concentrators of stress become liabilities; mining sequences to eliminate their formation or to develop predictable failure conditions must follow.

6. *The Time Factor* — The effect of time on the development of failure has been referred to. As the strength-stress ratio is reduced, time assumes greater importance. Some methods based on gradual rock failure require, within limits, that the time factor be predictable, figures 60 and 61.

7. *The Proximity of Other Orebodies* — Where substantial waste areas separate orebodies on the strike they usually can be mined without reference to each other except for consideration of access. When orebodies are close together on strike or are superimposed as parallel or branching bodies, pillar conditions between them can develop with mining. A stoping sequence may be desirable to avoid this. With such a sequence the stoping in one orebody should be well advanced with respect to the other. As noted earlier, in the case of open stopes it is preferable that the hangingwall be mined in advance of the footwall, but with filled stopes other factors may take precedence over this requirement.

8. *Grade of Deposit* — This will invite considerations as to the relative merits of selective and mass production methods. Low grade deposits as a rule demand mass production methods which frequently limit the percentage of recovery possible. On the other hand, high grade ore bodies require methods which ensure 100 per cent recovery, figure 86.

9. *Local Facilities — Labour and Materials* — Cheap labour does not necessarily mean low unit costs, but generally mining methods must be modified in detail for different parts of the world in accordance with the competency of available labour. Local availability of supporting materials such as timber and fill also will influence practice.

10. *Capital Available* — In mining, costs are of two types: capital and operating. If the funds for certain desirable capital expenditures are not available, operating costs will be higher as a result. If there is sufficient tonnage in sight, the higher initial capital cost of the alternative will be recoverable through lower operating costs. The judicious outlay of capital, when readily available, is always desirable. The difficulty arises in defining what is judicious in terms of developed and prospective ore at the various stages in the life of a mine.

Summary and Conclusions

The operational spectrum is subjected to all the pressures of the changing social and economic scenes. Higher wage rates and international competition demand greater efficiency measured in man and machine hours. These in turn demand mechanization and improvements in mine and open pit design which are reflected in mine openings and ground-control facilities. These shifting variables call for a continuous search for break-even points in all aspects of the operation. In this search the operator always must be guided by the safety limitations associated with ground control facilities.

5 | Stoping Methods

A General Classification of Underground Methods

The number of contexts within which most variables can appear introduces an element of confusion in any classification. The literature carries numerous expressions which have the merit of dividing methods into two or more groups. For instance, *track and trackless mining* are terms associated with increasing mechanization. Previously the accepted form of transport from stopes to the shaft or to the ore pass was usually rail (track) haulage. In certain cases this method now competes with trackless methods based on dump trucks, shuttle cars, load-haul-dump units, and occasionally conveyor belts. *Scraper mining* describes one method for the clearing of stopes into a chute or pass for the loading of transport vehicles. *Underhand and overhand methods* are a useful carry-over from hand drilling to distinguish faces advanced by down holes and those advanced by horizontal and / or up holes. *Open and filled stoping* indicates the absence or presence of filling in the operation. In open stopes the walls are, in general, self-supporting and open to inspection; in filled stopes they are not. *Advancing and retreating methods* have already been referred to.

All such distinctions, while grouping methods roughly, refer only to single characteristics and thus give little indication of the physical factors involved. It is perhaps impossible for any classification to embrace all the differences in practice flowing from the possible variations in physical conditions. However, a general classification should indicate the basic requirements for different methods. As noted earlier, ground control facilities are the primary consideration in the selection of a mining method and should be a distinguishing feature in any classification.

Each orebody with its geological associations imposes a different combination of basic factors from which, as a result of mining, ground conditions naturally flow.

These factors may be favourable or adverse. Even when favourable initially, bad ground conditions can result from the inept application of the most appropriate method.

In all mining operations, ground conditions gradually progress towards failure and within limits mining methods must be adaptable to such changes. In the process the ground control facilities of one method may gradually displace those of another. Thus, in practice methods are compromises with clear-cut demarcation lines only under ideal conditions.

The range in ground control which a classification must cover, varies from pillar support which provides for retaining the ground surrounding mining excavations rigidly in place in the course of mining, through varying degrees of controlled wall closure and subsidence, to the complete caving of an orebody and / or the overlying ground.

In figure 91 these three principles are represented by groups A, B, and C respectively, each of which forms the core of a larger circle within which satellite methods are grouped. The large central circle overlaps both the upper and lower circles indicating transition zones where some compromise with a basic principle is tolerable. The central circle carries inner circles, in the first case dividing supporting practice between filling methods and unit type supports. In the second circle the range of longwall practice is indicated. The lower circle also carries circles to distinguish between cover caving and the caving of ore.

The place of ore widths in the classification is indicated in the divisions outside the larger circles. *Generally narrow ore* includes widths up to about ten feet as this represents the range usually practicable with unit type supports. *Narrow to wide ore* has been introduced to cover room and pillar operations and shrinkage stoping which, except on a cost basis, are not particularly sensitive to ore width. Room and pillar operations on widths of less than five feet represent a compromise but they have been applied successfully on ore thicknesses up to 200 feet. Shrinkage stoping has been applied to widths varying from about five to more than 100 feet. *Generally wide ore* methods are appropriate with the widest ore but this does not exclude the possibility of filling methods on narrow ore. *Invariably wide ore* applies with methods which require widths of caving dimensions, usually in excess of 100 feet.

The dip of the orebody is a more elusive factor in the classification. Generally, for flat dips, room and pillar or one of the longwall methods will apply. For steep dips, excluding room and pillar, any of the methods might apply.

The strain energy accumulation scale to the right of the diagram is of interest. In Group A, with stoping spans and pillar loadings limited either by calculation or empiricism, the strain energy accumulation is under control. Over the transition zone and the pillar recovery phases, the methods involve increasing pillar loadings due to depth, the extension of the mining zone, or to reduction in pillar area. The increasing pillar loadings introduce a maintenance cost for openings involved and at some stage pillar failure either gradual or sudden follows. This is designated as a zone of increasing strain energy and as such, with the stronger rocks carries a *rockburst risk*. From the

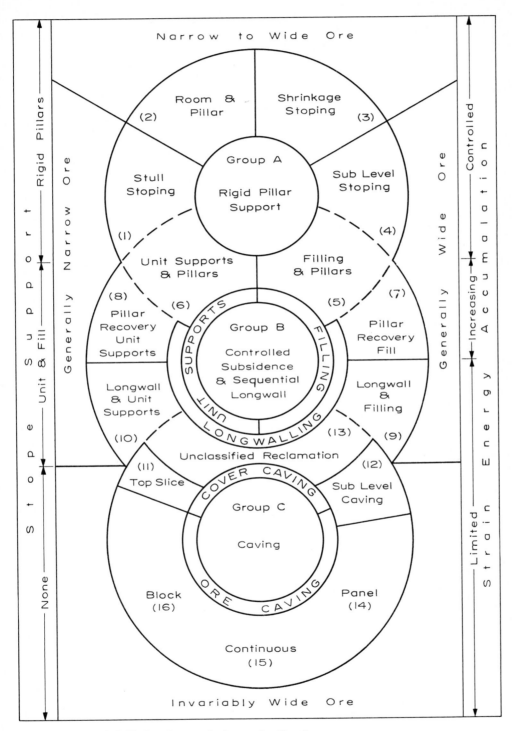

FIGURE 91 Stoping methods—a classification

centre of the middle circle to the bottom of the lower, progressive ground failure is a requirement of the various methods. Thus, except for the risks inherent with structural weaknesses, if ground failure follows its predicted course strain energy is released with failure and accumulations are thus limited.

GROUP A — RIGID PILLAR METHODS

Pillar-supported stopes, usually low-cost methods, have their widest application with the stronger rocks at shallow depth where strength-stress ratios provide adequate factors of safety. The variant in the strength-stress ratio may be the stress field. This can vary through a number of causes of which depth is one of the more obvious. Thus, for safe loading the percentage of pillar support will increase with depth and a point arrives when the proportion of the orebody necessarily allocated to pillar support becomes prohibitive. Alternatively, before this point is reached, ground conditions in the spans between pillars may force a modification of the method. In either case the trend is towards Group B methods with or without a transition phase. The result is that a ground control element, which adds to operating costs, appears in the mining cycle.

When the surface is expendable the end phase in pillar mining is the recovery of some or all of the pillar ore which has provided the basic ground control for the earlier operation.

GROUP B — LONGWALL METHODS

The longwall principles of ground control have been referred to and their application appears in the satellite methods of this group. Their use accepts the incompetency of rocks under prevailing stress conditions, but takes advantage of the fact that all rocks at the point of incipient failure can be supported to exert some control over the progress of failure and permit safe operating conditions for a limited time at the working face. Such support integrated with a longwall sequence, eliminating or minimizing stress concentrations associated with pillars and remnants, can result in predictable ground conditions as the face is advanced.

Due to the extensive and generally flat-lying nature of coal deposits, coal mining methods fall naturally into either the rigid pillar or longwall grouping. The latter methods have been widely developed over many years in the less-competent rocks of the coal measures. Their application with the harder rocks has been less prominent due to the moderate demands of more restricted orebodies at similar depth and because our understanding of ground control principles still continues as a gradual and empirical process.

There is an implied distinction between the use of support in these methods and in Group A methods. In Group A, given adequate pillar support, further support is introduced only on account of occasional loose which develops within an overall strength-stress ratio that ensures the competency of the rock mass as a whole. In most cases it is a protection against the inadequacy, or in some cases the necessity, of scaling operations as mining progresses. On the other hand, with the methods under discussion support is introduced under conditions of gradual failure in the rock mass as the ore is removed. Its purpose is to exert a degree of control before and after the failure which is deliberately induced by the mining operations.

In figure 91 below methods 5 and 6 longwall sequences may appear in some degree with all methods. Aside from any operating advantages which might follow, the principle involves extending a single stoping excavation by appropriate methods until it includes the full extent of the orebody. It will be apparent that if more than one excavation is involved pillar conditions necessarily follow, not always of a type where gradual failure can be assured.

GROUP C — CAVING METHODS

Ideally this classification differentiates between subsidence associated with cover caving and caving proper. Subsidence, within this context, implies that a failing hangingwall or roof is brought to rest, either on support or on the footwall, under sufficient control to ensure that there is little relative displacement within the subsiding mass. It may represent fracture zone development or it may be reflected in surface subsidence. On the other hand, with caving, on completion of the undercut support is eliminated and the height of the undercut permits uncontrolled movement of ruptured blocks to a degree which destroys the structural identity of the original mass and permits passing it as caved material through draw points below the cave.

This distinction may be subtle, but nevertheless in practice it is very real. Once we are forced out of open stoping conditions subsidence in some degree is unavoidable but caving is either deliberately or accidentally induced. Experience suggests that if an unsupported undercut of sufficient height to permit caving rather than subsidence is extended beyond certain limiting dimensions which depend on the stress pattern and the rock type, caving, predictable or otherwise, can be expected to follow. The progress of caving will depend on drawing off (shrinking) caved rock to eliminate support above the undercut and when necessary extending the undercut.

Caving thus represents a principle diametrically opposed to that underlying Group A methods. Instead of selectively ensuring that any particular zone remains rigidly in place or under some degree of control, once the caving undercut is complete natural forces are in control within the rather uncertain angles of break established by the undercut, figure 20. This statement requires qualification to the extent that some limited control over the timing of the caving is possible at the draw points.

The commercial application of the principle is limited to orebodies where caving is predictable over a specified undercut and results in caved material which can be passed economically through draw points below the undercut. For this latter requirement, and also for grade selectivity, caving and sub-level stoping are in competition.

The depth to which caving may be economical has yet to be determined. The controlling factors are likely to be the stress distribution, an ability to control the boundary of caving, and the maintenance cost on openings in the heaving zone below the undercut.

In summary and before discussing individual methods, it must be conceded in the absence of absolute yardsticks that any general classification will be influenced by the objective of the individual concerned. The above classification carries the thread of ground conditions through the range of possibilities. This permits a process of elimination based on available data. It also satisfies the "know why" of the mining problem and the "know how" then follows in the selection of facilities and equipment. This leads to a study of comparative costs. Also diagnostically, the contravention of basic principles can be readily distinguished from the inept application of a method.

Individual methods appear in figure 91 as satellite methods of groups A, B and C, numbered to distinguish the different principles. The methods included by no means exhaust the variations possible, but they do cover a range of practice within which most variations find a place.

Rigid Pillar Mining — Methods 1 to 4

STULL STOPING — METHOD 1

This method, figure 92, depends on pillars for mass support and upon stoping spans which are largely self-supporting. Stulls are installed in a geometric pattern to carry working floors, to form the base for chute and manway linings, and to support such local loose as may develop.

The method has been used on flat dips, but its widest application has been on steep dips where in narrow ore it competes with shrinkage stoping, perhaps most effectively in small orebodies and when wage rates are low. It does not require the broken reserve essential with shrinkage stoping, but compared with shrinkage stoping its greatest advantage is when widths are narrow enough to obstruct the free flow of shrinkage ore. This condition also involves the lowest unit cost for timber.

Through the stoping area the levels are carried on the crown pillars of stopes below and level intervals in continuous ore will vary from 100 to 150 feet.

The pillar structure must be based on a percentage of support which will ensure stability of the area as a whole. If the spans between crown pillars are excessive for the ground the horizontal span may be shortened by introducing rib pillars.

An overhand method is illustrated in figure 92 but it will be appreciated that there are underhand applications as well.

Occasionally in the final pulling of very narrow shrinkage stopes, as the ore is drawn down the placing of stulls follows in an effort to hold the walls in place and minimize dilution. This represents a compromise with stull stoping prior to a change of method usually from shrinkage to some form of cut-and-fill.

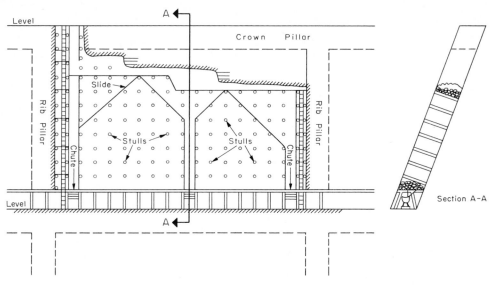

FIGURE 92 Stull stoping (narrow veins)

ROOM AND PILLAR MINING — METHOD 2

This terminology originates with coal mining but has gained a wide acceptance in metal mining also. If stopes and rooms are regarded as synonymous the expression could embrace the whole field of Group A. However, this offers difficulties in a general classification as one expects to walk through a room, but to climb through a stope so that it would seem appropriate to confine "room and pillar" to flat and gently dipping deposits.

In coal mining the terminology implies a more or less uniform spacing of rooms and pillars. In metal mining this also holds for the larger deposits, but in small orebodies a random distribution of pillars is often the case. Thus for this general classification room and pillar mining will apply to any arrangement of pillars designed to hold the roof or hangingwall rigidly in place on dips below those where the pillar structure is limited to the conventional sills, crowns, and ribs of metal mining practice.

The design of room and pillar layouts is still largely empirical, but rock mechanics has advanced to the degree where it contributes to a better understanding of the problem.

Estimates of pillar strength or loading must be accepted with reservations. However, if such data as appears in figure 64 is acceptable for comparative purposes a relationship between percentage support and pillar dimensions is apparent and from this a relationship with room span follows. Thus with conservative pillar loading, latitude is possible in co-ordinating room spans with rock properties and working requirements.

PLATE B A mobile aerial platform (Giraffe) in the context of figure 93. Note pillar walls and back. (*Courtesy of Gaspe Copper Mines Limited*)

Laboratory tests supported by practical experience suggest that in flat lying deposits, weaknesses such as joint or bedding planes, contacts and schistosity parallel to the orebody have little effect on the strength of pillars. Thus on flat dips square pillars giving shorter spans for a given percentage of support may have advantages. However, on steeper dips such weaknesses assume greater significance and when possible pillars should be lengthened to the dip, preferably with vertical or naturally arched down-dip faces. At some stage pillar support is best distributed by continuous pillars up and down dip.

Room and pillar methods are most common with bedded deposits. They have been applied with mining widths (thickness) varying from about 4 feet up to 200 feet. Equipment will vary with the headroom to the point where large units such as power shovels and dump trucks and load-haul-dump units are in competition.

Typical layouts are shown in figures 58 and 59. Figure 93 shows the Gaspe copper deposit where ore widths reach to 120 feet in the C or lower orebody.

SHRINKAGE STOPING — METHOD 3

In ground amenable to Group A methods shrinkage is perhaps the commonest method for steeply dipping lodes up to about 20 feet in width which are sufficiently regular in outline to permit gravity movement of the broken ore. As mentioned earlier the method competes with stull stoping on narrow widths and with long-hole sub-level stopes for widths above 20 feet.

Shrinkage stoping gets its name from the fact that a given volume of rock, in place, occupies about 60 per cent greater volume when broken. Thus in mining, working facilities at the face can be maintained by drawing off (shrinking) the excess volume of broken ore through chutes on the level below. The ore remaining in the stope is maintained at a level which permits its use as a working floor for each successive cut, until mining reaches the crown pillar stage. The accumulated ore is then drawn off as a single operation leaving an open excavation surrounded by crown, and / or sill pillars and rib pillars if necessary. The pillar-supported open excavation, as the end phase, justifies including the method with Group A.

It will be noted that an additional cost is involved in building up the broken ore reserve upon which the method depends.

The actual mining operation involves advancing a breast about 10 feet high for the full stope width along a flat back, usually by blasting horizontal holes 10 to 12 feet in length. The mining cycle is drilling, blasting, scaling, and rockbolting, accompanied by the periodic drawing down of broken ore to give a working height suitable for the next cut. Consistent with Group A practice the pillar support provided in the form of crowns and sills and ribs when desired should, except for occasional rockbolting, eliminate ground control from the mining cycle.

A less common method is to lay out the stope so that the back can be drilled over by long flat holes radiating from corner raises. However, with efficient sub-level methods as the alternative, this method would have a limited range of applications.

With the conventional method, using well-arched backs, stope widths in excess of 100 feet have been mined successfully. However, large stope widths do not necessarily provide the lowest cost. For lengths of wide ore which might justify a change of method the advantages of long hole sub-level stopes either longitudinal or transverse should be considered.

Certain rules concerning stope dimensions are developed later under sub-level

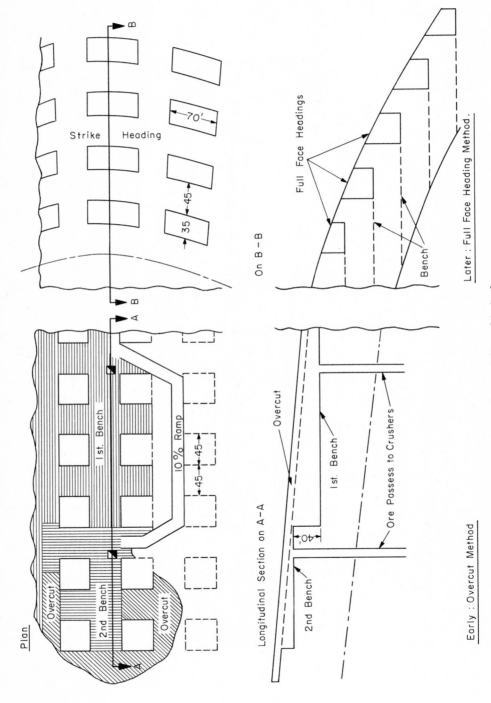

Plan

Strike Heading

70'

35 45

10% Ramp

45 45

Overcut

1st. Bench

2nd Bench

Overcut

On B – B

Full Face Headings

Bench

Later : Full Face Heading Method.

Longitudinal Section on A–A

Overcut

1st. Bench

2nd Bench

40'

Ore Passess to Crushers

Early : Overcut Method

FIGURE 93 A room and pillar method: Gaspe Copper Mines, Limited

PLATE C A 2 cubic yard shovel loading a 30 ton truck in the context of Figure 93. (*Courtesy of Gaspe Copper Mines Limited*)

stopes. These hold generally for steeply dipping ore over the Group A range, except that level intervals will vary with methods.

The width of ore is a factor in the variety of shrinkage layouts possible. In the narrower orebodies it is usual to sill out the stope at the level. This involves slashing the level to the full width of the ore, taking down the back to a height of about eighteen feet, installing the timber necessary for chutes, level support and the stope floor which carries the broken ore remaining in the stope. This method would be shrinkage on *timbered backs,* figure 94.

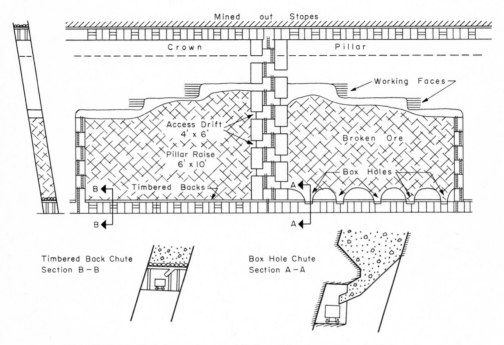

FIGURE 94 Shrinkage stoping (timbered backs and boxholes)

With wider ore there are advantages in eliminating much of this timber work by silling out the stope some distance above the level to leave a sill pillar between the stope floor and the level. Box holes as chutes at suitable intervals are raised from the level through this pillar and belled out to cover the stope floor. This would be a *box-hole shrinkage stope,* figure 94.

Some have considered that the periodic drawing of excess shrinkage ore as the stope progresses increases accident risks and adds to dilution from the walls. The alternative is to leave the main volume of broken ore standing undisturbed until the stope is completed when it can be drawn as a continuous operation over a limited period of time.

To accomplish this ore passes must be carried through the standing broken ore, through which the excess ore as broken can be passed to the chutes below. This adds the cut-and-fill ore handling practice to the shrinkage method. Locally the practice has been termed ore-filled shrinkage, but ore-pass shrinkage would be more appropriate as all shrinkage stopes are ore-filled during the mining operation. In special cases the practice would defer the transition to filling methods.

In shrinkage stoping, oversize, exposed as the ore is broken, can be blockholed in the stope. However, many large pieces are buried in the broken ore and if not broken as they are drawn down will obstruct loading at the chutes. Chutes should flow freely and any disruption of this process adds to costs. With wide ore this additional cost may justify more efficient alternatives. One method is to establish a scraper drift with access to the stope bottom through draw points. Large pieces can be blasted at the draw points before scraping to loading chutes. These latter chutes are well built with air-operated undercut arc gates and, with oversize elimi-nated, are capable of a predictable performance. A *scram drift shrinkage layout* is illustrated in figure 95 where the increased stope height is justified by ground condi-

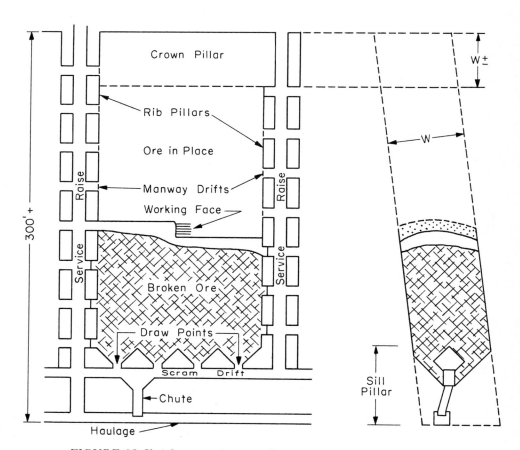

FIGURE 95 Shrinkage stoping over draw points

tions and an ability to deal with the additional tonnage through draw points. An alternative is to establish mucking-machine or scoop-tram draw points in crosscuts connecting to haulages in the hangingwall or footwall. With increasing ore width, the trend is towards long hole sub-level stopes and load-haul-dump facilities.

These various methods for ensuring the best flow of ore from shrinkage stopes are a matter of costs and tonnages available to individual draw points. They illustrate the principle that the extra cost of better facilities is always justified when sufficient tonnage is available for its recovery through savings in operating costs.

On the Witwatersrand at dips below the angle of repose shrinkage or semi-shrinkage stoping is applied in suitable cases. The practice is illustrated in figure 96. After the blast the excess volume of broken ore is scraped or lashed down the face while the remainder is left as support. At the back of this supporting pile a final recovery operation proceeds.

An early indication of ground pressure in shrinkage stopes is dilution from the walls. This leads to the replacement of shrinkage by flat back cut-and-fill within the same pillar framework, method 5. In due course when a maintenance problem with or without rockbursts appears in openings through the pillars, method 9, providing a longwall sequence to eliminate pillar formation, becomes appropriate.

SUB-LEVEL STOPING — METHOD 4

These methods, in modern practice, are largely confined to steep dips and to orebodies permitting either long-hole benching or ring drilling practice. They require extra development and, in competition with shrinkage stoping, both long-hole facilities and favourable unit development costs require wide ore.

The optimum main level interval is a compromise between costs and dilution. Development unit costs vary inversely with the level interval but some costs and the possibility of dilution vary directly, the latter being particularly obvious in open stope pillar recovery.

The greater wall area usually exposed in longitudinal stopes is likely to result in greater percentage dilution than with transverse stopes. On the other hand, with transverse stoping layouts the pillar structure usually represents somewhat more than 50 per cent of the ore as compared with a much lower proportion for longitudinal stopes. In either case the vertical height at which the ore rests after a pillar blast depends partly on the level interval and may influence final recovery. In practice, with these methods in good ground the compromise between costs and recovery points to a main level interval ranging from 300 to 400 feet, but intermediate service levels at mid-height are frequently justified. To maintain burdens sub-levels are spaced so that holes do not exceed about 100 feet.

Longitudinal Stopes — This practice is limited to sections where the ore width does not exceed an optimum operating width which in good ground usually ranges between 60 and 70 feet. This width represents the maximum desirable undercut for crown pillars and there is little to be gained in breaking efficiency from greater widths. Thus when ore width exceeds this range a change to transverse stoping is indicated.

Prior to pillar recovery a crown pillar stands undercut for the whole stope area and while caving dimensions must be avoided some sloughing is tolerable. As a protection to openings above the crown, a good rule is that the depth of crown should approximate the stope width. The effective stope height is thus related to the width, figure 97.

With longitudinal stopes the strike length represents unsupported walls. This dimension is arbitrary, but with a level interval of 300 feet as a first approximation, 150 feet can be regarded as a reasonable length. This will be established by rib pillars, the breadth or strike length of which can be related to the stope width. The advantage of a short stope length is more positive control. Against this, over the orebody as a whole somewhat more raising may be required and there is a higher proportion of pillar ore.

Transverse Stopes — These, running from hangingwall to footwall, have a length limited to the ore width or to a maximum of about 250 feet. When the ore width exceeds 250 feet it is good practice to introduce a longitudinal pillar to shorten the stope length and support the rib pillars establishing the stope width.

An optimum operating width between 60 and 70 feet has been referred to for longitudinal stopes. Except for adverse structure similar widths hold for transverse stopes. As the stope width is one of the critical dimensions in stope design, when it is arbitrary, as in transverse stopes, there is little to be gained in reaching for a maximum. Pillar and stope ore vary little in cost assuming a suitable mining sequence, and again the best that can be gained by increased stope width is the elimination of a few raises over the orebody as a whole. Against this is the possibility of the loss of access ways over crown pillars and the psychological effects of loss of predictability in pillar areas.

The size of rib pillars separating these transverse stopes is also arbitrary. The first consideration is the inherent stability of a pillar 300 feet or more in height reaching from the hangingwall to the footwall. As referred to earlier longitudinal vertical pillars are introduced to limit this width. In practice, within this limitation the rib pillar breadth (strike length) should be not less than about one-third of the effective hangingwall to footwall dimension with a minimum of about forty feet when service openings are required in the pillar.

This type of mining is a mass production method with which some flexibility is desired. The foregoing dimensions referring to rather ideal conditions are no more than a guide. However, the best overall costs and ore recovery will be associated with the best ground control. Local ground conditions are the dominating factor and within this context, when dimensions are arbitrary as for stopes and pillars, predictability, and thus efficiency, improves with moderation in the choice of dimensions.

With transverse stopes the strike length of a stope and pillar constitutes a

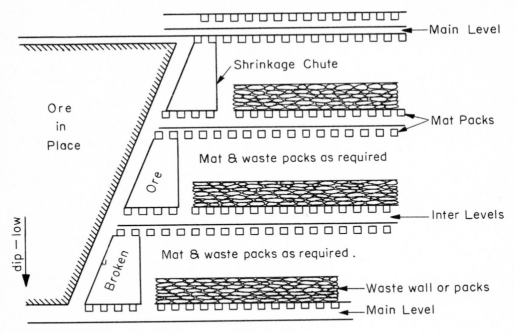

FIGURE 96 Shrinkage stoping (Witwatersrand)

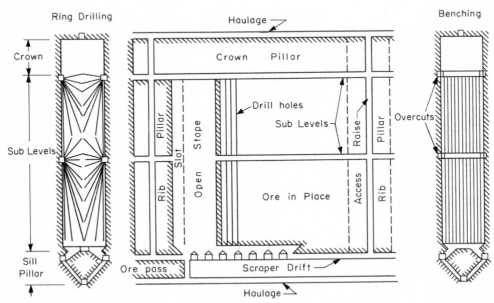

Note : The trend is for load-haul-dump units to displace scrapers

FIGURE 97 Sub-level stoping

unit for stope development purposes. Frequently this length is evenly divided between stope and pillar, but occasionally when pillar recovery can follow immediately behind the stoping there are advantages in having the pillar somewhat larger than the stope. For a given unit length this tends to strengthen the stope crown and the pillar can be reduced by slashing prior to the final pillar and crown blast.

Within the same pillar pattern ring drilling and benching are alternatives.

Benching, figure 97 — In steeply dipping deposits this method has the advantage of evenly spaced down holes giving a uniform powder distribution and ideal breaking conditions. However, for drilling, men work in an overcut exposing the bench for the full stope width and forward drilling is limited to the advance of the overcut. Safety belts are required when working on benches, the security of which depends upon an absence of slips and weaknesses which could affect their stability.

In the U.S.S.R. a stope and pillar layout has been developed which permits heavier drilling equipment, larger holes, and increased forward drilling. Larger holes should result in lower breaking costs, but as compared with face ore overcut ore is expensive and the merit of this practice depends on the break-even points with conventional methods. For break-even points between hole size and costs, the large holes included in current practice at Texasgulf's Kidd Creek (91) and INCO's Ontario Division operations (92) are examples.

Ring Drilling, figure 97 — This operation can be carried out in the comparative safety of a drilling drift where the amount of forward drilling is limited only by the risk of losing holes through shifting ground as the operation progresses.

Sub-level intervals depend, amongst other factors, on the depth to which the direction of holes can be controlled to ensure correct spacing and burden at the toes. In practice with percussion drill holes longer than 100 feet uncertainty develops in this respect. However, this length together with up holes of about sixty feet permits a wide range of choice to arrive at the best cost pattern.

In transverse stopes two drilling drifts per stope per sub-level are common. These permit holes along the pillar to give regular walls. Alternatively in a compromise with development costs single drilling drifts on some sub-levels are possible. However, careless work in this operation or in upward drilling to establish crowns leaves a risk of bootleg holes for pillar drilling.

On the basis of safety, costs, and flexibility, practice at present appears to favour ring drilling rather than benching. However the large holes referred to at Texasgulf and INCO may change this preference.

These methods, depending as they do on large stope dimensions, are very sensitive to ground pressure. In the classification under Group A, they are not dependent on longwall sequences. However, in practice in wide and extensive orebodies the ideal seldom applies and time and the effects of subsequent mining on such pillar structures requires consideration. In those cases, where up to 50 per cent of the orebody may be allocated to pillar structures, a sequence to stoping which permits the open stope removal of recoverable pillars on the completion of the stopes they are designed to protect, is likely to ensure the best recovery of ore. Alternatively, if the grade of the orebody justifies the cost, on completion stopes can be filled and satisfactory results can be expected from filling methods of pillar recovery.

At the MacLeod Mine of the Algoma Steel Corporation Limited, Wawa, Ontario, there is an interesting example of the open stope mining of an orebody some 5000 feet in length, dipping about 70 degrees and ranging up to 350 feet in width. The first mining was by open pit to a depth of about 350 feet, followed by a caving lift of 300 feet. Quite aside from the dilution associated with caving, the method permitted little selectivity as to grades and mix. For these reasons, and also the low grade of the ore, below the caving the orebody was laid out for long-hole sub-level mining with transverse stopes 60 feet in width separated by pillars 80 feet in breadth, on main level intervals of 300 feet.

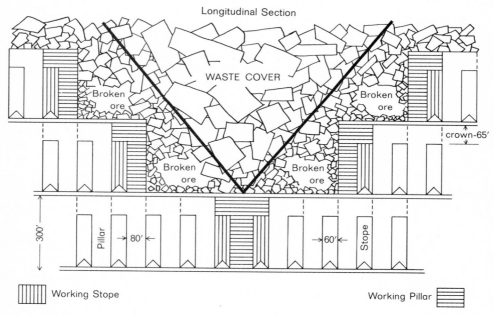

FIGURE 98 Transverse sub-level stopes in sequence

With the first underground mining breaking through to the open pit, a rigorous sequence was established based on mining from the top down with the mined area assuming the "V" outline as shown in figure 98. This ensured solid ground below each operating stope and pillar, and permitted the mining of pillars as soon as stopes into which they could be blasted became available. Figure 98 is a generalized longitudinal section showing the essential features of the operation. It will be noted, with the sequence inviting caving above as mining proceeds below, that a waste cover soon develops over the operation.

A rib and a crown pillar are blasted as a unit, comprising some hundreds of thousands of tons. With the blast confined under the waste cover the ore is thrown on the draw points to a height somewhat greater than the mining width, and the waste cover adjusts and follows the operation downwards. The surface effects of this essential feature are shown on page 2.

With the broken ore occupying the corner formed by the end of ground and the crown pillar below, the immediate walls are partially supported as the drawing of ore proceeds from the ore / waste interface towards the end of ground or operating pillar. This, assisted by draw control, ensured a maximum recovery.

Product tolerances are narrow, but some thirty million tons have been mined by the method to a depth of about 1500 feet with little detectable dilution and considerable flexibility as to grades and mix. Recovery from stopes approximates 100 per cent with somewhat less from pillars. There are no pillars standing more than two lifts in height and these are readily recoverable at the convenience of the operation. This leaves the ore reserve in place on both sides of the "V" and generally free of pillar structures. Figure 86 shows the trend in break-even points with varying grades, costs, and recoveries for different options that might be competitive in any particular context.

The foregoing methods, representative of Group A, are characteristic of the self-supporting phase of the stronger rocks. With increasing ground pressure regardless of its source, failure conditions resulting in fracture zones develop in stope walls and pillar stability enters a less predictable phase. This eliminates the self-supporting aspect inherent in Group A and forces a transition to methods of Group B.

Transitional Options — Methods 5 and 6

These methods are transitional between the pillar-supported methods of Group A and the sequential longwall methods of Group B. They are introduced to control failure in the walls while the pillar structure is still adequate. In wide ore, dilution and maintenance problems usually emphasize the desirability of filling, method 5. In narrow ore stulls with headboards gradually prove inadequate and compressible supports such as crib sets, mat packs, and, on the flatter dips, waste walls or thin pillars designed for failure are substituted, method 6.

The situation will deteriorate with increasing depth and extraction and failure in both walls and pillars will require additional support and maintenance. If the failure is gradual, risks are limited to extra costs and the possibility of losing ore and current methods can continue until the cost pattern suggests alternatives. On the other hand, if rockbursts become a hazard a longwall sequence is desirable at the earliest opportunity.

Some facilities of Group B methods may be combined with Group A practice to extend the life of the latter. Examples are: ore passes in shrinkage stopes to avoid loosening the walls by the intermittent pulling of chutes below the broken shrinkage ore; cut-and-fill mining with the crown, sill, and rib pillars of shrinkage stoping; the use of pillars designed for failure as in figure 61 and the early removal of pillars, in sequence, as in figure 98.

Pillar Recovery — Methods 7 and 8

These methods, generally including a sequence or longwall aspect, differ only in the method of support. When the surface is expendable one or other of these operations represent the end phase of all earlier methods.

Pillar recovery with filling methods, with and without square sets, is a reasonably standardized operation both as to overhand and underhand methods. Heavy ground is to be expected but with skilled miners steady progress is usually assured for the recovery of close to 100 per cent of the ore. When pillars have been crushed or weakened, underhand methods with cemented fill now compete successfully with overhand methods (86).

Open stope mining methods usually permit open stope pillar recovery with unit-type supports, with the loss of some ore. However, when the grade of pillar ore is high, economics may suggest filling the stopes to permit the higher recovery likely to follow with filling methods.

Open stope pillar recovery practice covers the requirements of flat dips with pillar heights ranging from the minimum to well over 100 feet, and also of steeper dips from the narrow pillar structures of stull stoping to structures representing 50 per cent of the orebody when transverse sub-level stopes are involved.

No single procedure is characteristic of this range and few can be discussed out of context. Each operation is usually a specialized problem strongly influenced by local conditions. There are numerous references to the subject in the technical press but in general, when long-hole drilling has an application this practice is favoured. Exceptions are to be noted when ground conditions permit only the robbing, rather than the recovery, of pillars.

Finally the timing of open stope pillar recovery should again be emphasized. It is frequently possible to mine to a sequence which permits the recovery of individual pillars as the operation progresses, figure 98. Failing some planning in this respect with the early stoping, a slow deterioration of the pillar structure, resulting in loss of ore, is a common occurrence.

Longwall — Sequential Mining — Methods 9 and 10

LONGWALL AND FILL — METHOD 9

With this method, we pass from the range of competent rigid pillar support to that of positive, and to some degree predictable, ground failure. Pillars, remnants, and weaknesses as concentrators of stress have become liabilities to be avoided as far as possible by longwall methods. However, the supporting value of small pillars, designed for failure on a time basis, is recognized and retained.

Stope dimensions have been discussed under sub-level stoping, which applies only in the open stope range where ground is adequately competent. As the ground becomes incompetent due to pressure conditions or geological causes, filling methods become desirable in the wider orebodies and a longwall sequence is added to provide the best possible pressure distribution. Under these conditions stope dimensions must be revised downwards. In steeply dipping orebodies with filling, from a supporting point of view the stope width becomes a critical dimension. The optimum width is that which in conjunction with a suitable length, permits the maximum output per man-shift or in some cases the most rapid vertical progress of the stope. It will be apparent that in arriving at this length and width a compromise is necessary with quite a number of variables, including ground control and mechanization. For longitudinal stopes the mining width is the ore width up to the optimum width, which under pressure conditions may be less than 25 feet. For greater ore widths transverse stopes and pillars are the usual alternative. However, with the most cohesive consolidated fill, costs decide on the merit of transverse stopes or longitudinal stopes in sequence across the width of the orebody with no separating pillars.

Operating efficiency is dependent on close adherence to an optimum width for local ground conditions. At Noranda's Horne Mine 40 foot pillars were divided into three slices for mining with a consolidating slag fill with a much better output per man-shift than was possible when the full 40 feet was mined in one pass.

Flat Back Overhand Methods — These methods follow the conventional shrinkage practice in breaking ground, but ore passes at suitable intervals to which broken ore can be scraped or hauled on the working floor must be carried upward through the fill, figure 99. Scraping ore and the placing of fill are additions to the shrinkage cycle at the expense of output per man-shift. If square sets are added also, a further reduction in output per man-shift follows.

To avoid sill pillars, under pressure conditions stopes are silled out at the level to conform with a longwall sequence. With mined ground above a level, longitudinal flat-back stopes working upwards towards this level create a longitudinal pillar and thus a critical stress concentration early in their progress. For this reason, except when working upwards towards unmined ground, the long flat backs possible with method 5 are avoided in favour of lengths of about 100 feet. These are usually continued through any crown pillar stage in shortened lengths with or without the use of square sets. With increasing ground pressure, vertical slice square-set stopes, in sequence level to level, are the ultimate expression of the above practice.

There is a break-even point between the ideal stope length for fully mechanized cut-and-fill mining and the shorter length and sequence desirable with deteriorating ground conditions. Judgement in such matters must lean on local experience.

In the past square-set cut-and-fill was the most costly, but also in many cases, the ultimate method when all others had failed. In the progressive deterioration of

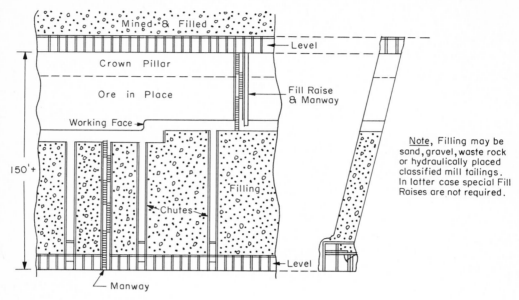

FIGURE 99 Flat back cut and fill stope

Note, Filling may be sand, gravel, waste rock or hydraulically placed classified mill tailings. In latter case special Fill Raises are not required.

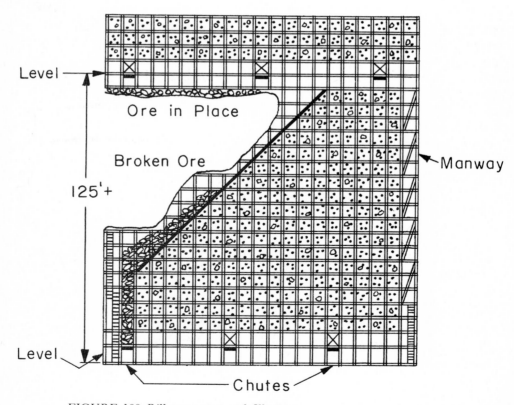

FIGURE 100 Rill square set and fill stope

ground leading to square-setting, timber posts, cap sets, cribs, and mechanical props have all been used to support the back, sometimes beyond the break-even point for square-set practice. More recently the importance of an optimum stoping width, as described earlier, has been recognized. Within this context rock bolts and wire mesh netting in many cases supersede square-set practice.

A post-pillar method of support has been developed at Falconbridge to meet the requirements of an earlier layout (93). It provides for carrying pillars from the footwall upwards through the fill to support the back. It competes with other methods for supporting the wide backs and also with the concept of optimum stoping width. The method has much in its favour but break-even points, weighted for grade and recovery, will determine its appropriate range.

Underhand Methods — Filling methods were discussed under support, but largely with an eye to overhand practice. An *underhand method* was developed at INCO (94) in the first instance, to recover crushed pillars where the productivity with square-set and fill was low. The practice has now progressed, in conjunction with cemented fill, to the point where it has a wide application (86), particularly in competition with square-set and fill (figures 101 and 102).

Transverse Stopes (Overhand Cut-and-Fill — When ore widths exceed the optimum referred to above, usually in the ±25 foot range, the optimum width is retained by laying out the stope length transversely, hangingwall to footwall, rather than longitudinally in the plane of the lode. In these cases, the stope width is defined by a rib pillar which supports the brow and acts as a temporary division between stopes. However, such rib pillars may not be required with a good consolidating fill.

Transverse cut-and-fill stopes also may be silled out at the level to conform with a sequence and progress to the level above leaving no crown. Thus the only pillar structure is the rib pillar between stopes. This usually is cut to a strike length that will ensure early failure, but which also is adequate for efficient pillar recovery by either overhand or underhand methods.

Resuing — Within pillar-supported panels resuing is a compromise between methods 5 and 6. With the longwall application it is a compromise between methods 9 and 10, but the filling aspect is only incidental to the method.

This method, figure 103, applies on any dip when the ore width is well below the minimum stoping width. It requires an effective parting between the ore and one of its walls to break to. The stope is opened out to an optimum working width by removing the ore and waste in separate operations. The ore is passed to a chute and the waste, the volume of which can be varied with the stope width, is disposed of as fill behind the operation. The method on a competitive basis is reserved for a special condition and is obviously rather sensitive to wage rates.

Rill Stoping — This originally referred to an otherwise overhand stope face inclined to permit its advance by down-hole drilling. The terminology derives from

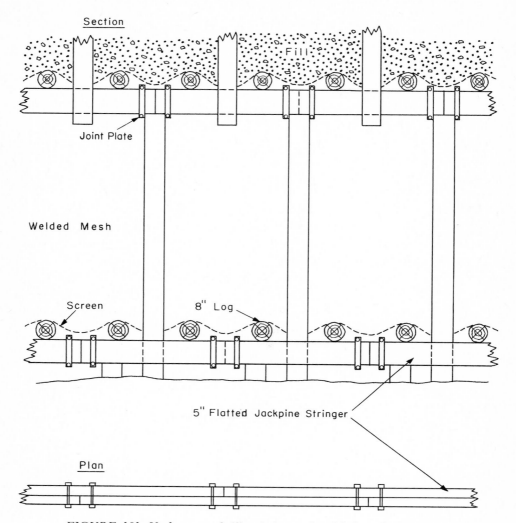

FIGURE 101 Undercut and fill—timber and welded mesh screen mats. (*After McCreedy and Hall*[86])

hand drilling practice when stope design was oriented around four-foot holes. Its problematical place in competitive modern mining is largely confined to a special adaptation of square-set and fill mining, figure 100.

Here, an overhand rill face can be established parallel to a floor carried along the diagonal of the square-sets, with the set dimensions thus governing the slope. It varies from the conventional square-set and fill in that mining is to an inclined rather than to a flat back and the removal of broken ore is arranged accordingly. The advantages of such a face are that it facilitates the movement of broken ore and, as regards pressure conditions, it is intermediate between the flat-back and vertical-slice methods. Its disadvantages are obvious.

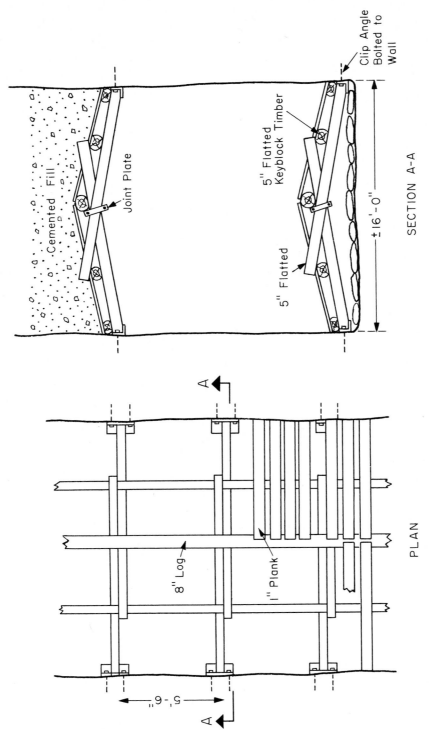

Clip Angle Bolted to Wall

Cemented Fill

Joint Plate

5" Flatted Keyblock Timber

5" Flatted

±16'-0"

SECTION A-A

A

8" Log

1" Plank

5'-6"

A

PLAN

FIGURE 102 Scissor set. Undercut and fill[86]

PLATE D Drilling in a mechanized cut-and-fill stope, Frood Mine. (*Courtesy of INCO*)

LONGWALL AND UNIT SUPPORT — METHOD 10

This covers a variety of closely related practices. Figures 60 and 104 show typical coal mine applications where operating facilities and ground control practice are apparent.

PLATE E An undercut and fill stope. (*Courtesy of INCO*)

Figure 104 illustrates packing and chocking with timber-face support. Hydraulic or friction props with a link bar system and powered supports are alternatives. A composite of several hydraulic props constructed to form a mobile support unit is referred to as a powered support (88). These are advanced by mechanical means and the initial cost for a four-foot coal seam is about twice that for the individual

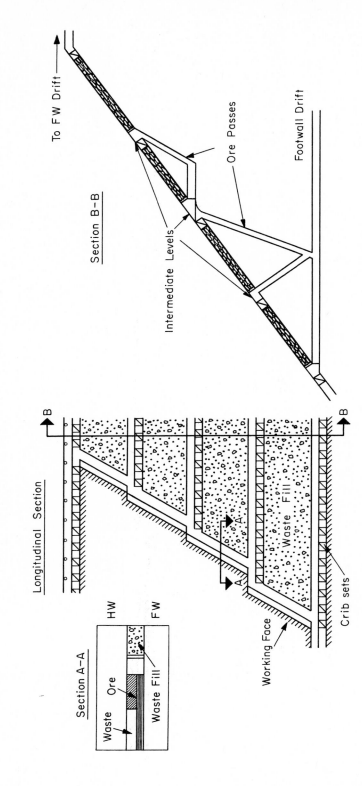

To FW Drift

Section B-B

Ore Passes

Footwall Drift

Intermediate Levels

Longitudinal Section

B

B

Waste Fill

A

A

Working Face

Crib sets

Section A-A

HW

FW

Waste

Ore

Waste Fill

FIGURE 103 Resuing

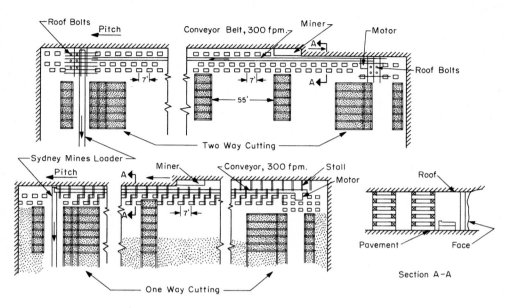

Ref.   Doxey, trans AIME. Vol. 199, 1954: see also Ref. 95, 1965

FIGURE 104 Supports on a longwall coal face

hydraulic prop and link bar system. They have advantages in man-hours as compared with the individual props including the elimination of waste walls (89).

Figure 61 illustrates another modification of methods 6 and 10 as developed in the Michigan copper area on dips of ±30 degrees. In this case, except for occasional posts and rockbolts, support is by small pillars about 5 feet by 15 feet which serve as temporary supports, as stopes averaging about 10 feet in height are taken through to the level above. As the stopes advance, the pillars retain some supporting value until ultimately, with complete failure, the subsidence or caving of the hangingwall follows at a safe distance behind the working faces.

In other mines locally, no doubt due to slightly different ground and economic factors, a similar result was obtained by uniformly spaced heavy-stull support.

Caving Methods — Methods 11 to 16

TOP SLICING — METHOD 11

This method refers to the mining of an orebody from the top down by a succession of horizontal slices about 10 feet high progressing as sequential longwall cuts below a timber mat. With the cover rock subsiding with each cut it is an extension of method 10. However, as the single cut of method 10 may only result in subsidence, the successive cuts of top slicing ultimately result in the caving of

PLATE F A load-haul-dump unit. A scooptram with a 5 cubic yard bucket. (*Courtesy of INCO*)

the cover rock. The method thus finds a place in the transition phase between Groups B and C. Similarities with underhand cut-and-fill are to be noted.

The method is limited to that type of ground which precludes overhand mining as the back cannot be relied upon for self-support over limited mining spans. The cover rock is separated from the mining operation and controlled by a timber mat reinforced with wire mesh screening. The mat is established on the first cut. As the cut advances supporting timbers behind the face are pulled to induce an even subsidence. With the mat established this timber and that on subsequent cuts is left to reinforce it. The method had its widest application with certain types of iron ore of the above nature and with which block caving was unsatisfactory due to the recompacting or clay-like quality of the ore. The control provided permits mining to a grade approximating that of the ore in place. The price of this selectivity is a sensitivity to wage rates which only mechanization can overcome.

Figure 105 illustrates the process from which the nature of operating facilities and ground control will be apparent.

SUB-LEVEL CAVING — METHOD 12 (Ref. 96)

This method is a natural development from top slicing. The mat is eliminated, the cut is deepened to about 25 feet, and the amount of level development

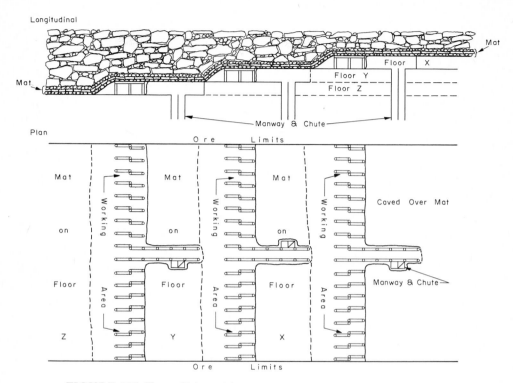

FIGURE 105 Top splicing with mat

decreases proportionately. The cut is removed by mining an undercut and caving the remainder of the ore with the assistance of blasting and cover weight. Its place in ore caving, as compared with cover caving, depends upon the proportion of ore involved in the caving process. It is suitable in orebodies which are not appropriate for block caving.

Due to the limited floor intervals the method can follow irregular ore outlines on the dip more effectively than is possible with the deeper lifts of block caving. On the other hand, the method is less selective than top slicing due to the absence of a mat and the dilution which follows, but on overall recovery is likely to be more selective than block caving. Figure 106 illustrates the highly mechanized method.

UNCLASSIFIED RECLAMATION WORK — METHOD 13

This place has been reserved in recognition of the fact that most mining methods, particularly those dependent on rigid pillars for success, can go wrong. This may be due to rockbursts or to a gradual increase in maintenance costs with deteriorating ground conditions and may involve extensive areas.

If the amount of ore left standing justifies the cost, the reclamation of the area may be considered. As indicated by its position in figure 91 the methods involved,

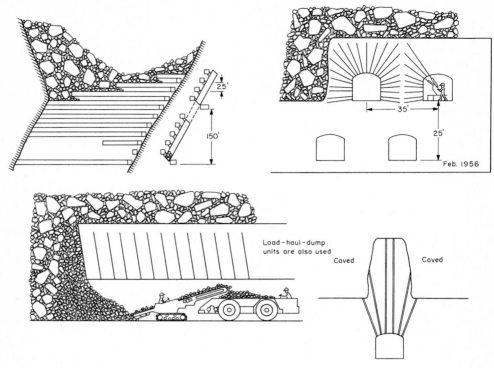

FIGURE 106 Sub-level caving (*Kiruna*)[96]

in addition to re-development, may represent any combination of Group B and the cover caving of Group C.

PANEL, CONTINUOUS, AND BLOCK CAVING — METHODS 14, 15, AND 16

These are mass production methods referred to earlier which, when suitably applied, result in the lowest possible unit mining cost.

Caving heights sometimes may be limited by estimated angles of break, but, otherwise, due to the cost per square foot for developing the undercut and openings below are seldom less than 200 and commonly about 400 feet in height.

In block caving the development of the undercut, varying up to about 200 feet square, draw points, and scraper drifts is very similar to that required with wide shrinkage and sub-level open stopes. Development in the vertical plane, at least for the initial operation, takes the form of fringe drifts and corner raises to influence the line of break, and when required, boundary stopes to further weaken the walls and commence the initial cave.

Panel and continuous caving are terms usually applied with a continuously extending undercut in panel units or otherwise.

Caving competes with transverse sub-level stopes with which, as noted above, the undercut and draw-point preparation has common features. The sub-level stopes are an alternative when explosive consumption at draw points becomes excessive and when a degree of grade selectivity, not present with caving, is possible. The development of a caving block is shown in figure 107.

It will be noted that longwall with unit support, top slicing, sub-level, and block caving form a continuous progression from Group B to Group C.

GENERAL REMARKS

The foregoing methods, which cover most of the world's mining, have all been developed empirically and usually with little knowledge of any theory involved. The classification rests more on the "know why" aspect of the problems than on the "know how." The "know how" can be gained only in the field of practical experience, but without the "know why" its contribution to good judgement is very limited indeed.

The fact that most mining operations proceed on a predictable course only emphasizes the exceptional cases. These occur in the grey zone between the essentials for different methods and reflect our confusion in the assessment of the variables involved. In a qualitative sense, rock mechanics has contributed much to our understanding of the problems of ground control. Quantitatively, however, the position is less satisfactory. Nevertheless, the progress of our knowledge in recent years leaves the impression that the mining engineer who is not conversant with "the state of the art" at any time may well be working under a self-imposed handicap.

Mining Costs

In Canada three mining methods currently account for 81 per cent of the ore mined by underground methods: room and pillar, largely in potash, 31 per cent; cut-and-fill, 27 per cent; and open stoping, largely long-hole, 23 per cent — leaving only 19 per cent for all other methods, (97). This result is influenced by the nature of the orebodies and also by the wage structure in Canadian operations. More labour-intensive methods would be probable with lower wage rates and / or less mechanization.

A mining method represents a compromise with numerous variables and operating costs will vary accordingly. The classification based on ground control can be seen in the best perspective when the dollar sign is superimposed. However, except for specific comparisons, this is difficult as the perspective is clouded by variations in orebodies, in operating conditions and, in particular, by inflationary effects and

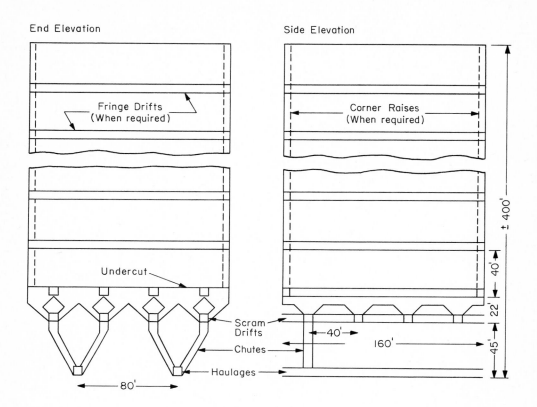

End Elevation

Fringe Drifts
(When required)

Side Elevation

Corner Raises
(When required)

Undercut

Scram Drifts

Chutes

Haulages

80'

40'

160'

± 400'

40'

22'

45'

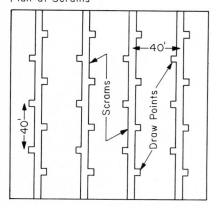

Plan at Scrams

40'

40'

Scrams

Draw Points

FIGURE 107 Block caving

Scraping may be directly to cars just below the scrams, to chutes between scrams and haulage or to an ore pass system leading to crusher. There is also a trend towards load haul dump facilities.

improving productivity. Generally, up to an optimum, the wider the ore the greater the choice of methods, and the higher the grade the greater the preference for high-cost selectivity. Within this overall context, perhaps the simplest meaningful comparison is to rank methods in the order of increasing costs, as follows;

> Open pit
> Block caving
> Sub-level stoping
> Sub-level caving
> Room and pillar mining
> Shrinkage stoping
> Special cut-and-fill*
> Top slicing
> Overhand cut-and-fill**
> Underhand cut-and-fill
> Square-set and fill
> Very narrow stoping
> (Stull, shrinkage, and resue)

With the lower cost methods, lost ore has a place in break-even point comparisons. With the advent of dilution due to ground pressure it has been common practice to adjust from an open to a filled-stope method with a substantial cost increase. If open stoping can be placed on a sequence there are times when it might be profitable to accept the dilution and increase mill capacity to deal with it. The break-even point between acceptable dilution and the best alternative is always an interesting speculation, figure 86.

Summary and Conclusions

Mining methods are compromises weighted for the effects of the dimensions of orebodies, the properties of rocks and rock masses, materials and labour costs, the grade of orebodies, and mechanical and ground control facilities. There are few absolute yardsticks associated with any of these variables and the choice of a method, in the final analysis, thus depends upon judgement. This, in turn, is best based on a perspective over a wide range of knowledge and experience. In this perspective the first priority should be given to ground control facilities upon which the success of every mining method depends.

------

*With competent ground and physical conditions permitting ideal layouts for the use of the best drilling and load-haul-dump units.
**With varying ground conditions and scraping to mill holes in stopes.

6 | Rockbursts

Cause and effect

A rockburst may be defined as the rupture due to natural forces of a volume of rock *in situ* in such a manner that the energy release can be recorded as a distinct and abnormal seismic event.

Sounds attributed to rock failure and the gradual extension of fracture zones are common in deep mines. They have seismic reflections which may be distinct, but are in no sense abnormal. In practice, the term rockburst has been reserved to describe phenomena more unusual than the so-called gradual working of ground associated with fracture zone development. The rate and amount of energy released, reflected in the frequency and amplitude of the seismic waves, is the distinguishing feature with the lower limits being a matter of opinion.

The effects also include the sudden redistribution of stress trajectories and the consequential extension of fracture and relaxing zones. Here it is relevant to note that explosive technology has demonstrated that the energy from a longitudinal wave, reflected at a free surface, can induce extensive tensile failure parallel to the free surface. Such failure, though secondary to the initial failure which generated the seismic activity, may represent some of the damage associated with major rockbursts.

The cause of the initial failure in rockbursts is, of course, the straining of a rock mass beyond its elastic limit. As the process is largely concealed within the rock walls of a mine any explanation is dependent on theoretical considerations consistent with the properties and structure of the rock mass and with the stress distribution around openings involved. This directs attention to the theory of elasticity, to probable stresses in shear or tension on the periphery of mine openings or their fracture zones, and to the geometry and structure to which they are related (98).

Rockbursts are usually associated with the more brittle, elastic rock types, planes of weakness, and extremes in stress concentration. The latter are most conspicuous with the high axis ratios pertaining to the narrower orebodies. The most prolific rockburst areas are probably under great tectonic strain, but few deep mines completely escape the hazard.

Early experience also has associated major rockbursts with pillar-supported areas in a late but uncoordinated stage of extraction. This practice applied over the range of flat to steep dips. The usual progression was to develop a mining area in blocks, or for flat-back stoping to floor pillars. Mining then progressed without regard to sequence until, at a late stage of extraction, individual blocks were reduced to pillars with rapidly increasing loads. At some stage in a progression of minor rockbursts a major rockburst, affecting much of the mining area, followed.

With a heterogeneous rock mass and the many conditions of geometry, loading, and structure possible, even the most gradual failure frequently defies precise analysis. The data available from rockbursts is usually less satisfactory for isolating specific mechanisms.

Mines operate under ground pressures which are usually more complicated than the simple gravity load. In any case, mining is a process of decompressing a volume of rock which bears an exponential relationship to the mined area, figure 55. This process, reflected in the free faces of an excavation and the consequential adjustments to the compression, relaxing, and fracture zones, is the background upon which problems leading to rockbursts are superimposed; the greater the decompression involved, the more numerous the problems.

Predictability

The United States Bureau of Mines has had some limited success in associating microseismic activity with the prediction of rockbursts (99). However, general acceptability requires further development of the principle and refinements in interpretations. In the meantime there is no universally accepted method for the prediction of rockbursts as to time, but within some structural and geometric contexts, a limited predictability is possible as to place.

Recently, a change in the ratio of the velocity of the P and S seismic waves has been detected preceding earthquakes (100). How reliable this may be as a means of prediction, and whether it applies also with rockbursts remains to be established.

Strain Energy

Many years ago J. S. Jones (101) in studying rockbursts on the Kolar gold field estimated from seismographic records that the medium heavy rockbursts experienced there released seismic energy of the order of 15×10^6 foot-tons. More recently a figure of 50×10^6 foot-tons has been given for some of the heavy rockbursts on the Witwatersrand (102) and Cook (103) has given estimates for a range of seismic events closely related to the advance of mining faces. A severe rockburst at Kirkland Lake, Ontario, recorded at Boston, 580 miles away, was estimated by Coates (104) at 19×10^6 foot-tons. The Merker's rockburst in Germany in 1958 also was recorded on seismographs from Moscow to southern Spain (105). For the bump or rockburst at Springhill, Nova Scotia in 1958 (106), seismic energy has been estimated at only 37×10^3 foot-tons within a factor of 10. This much lower estimate for such a catastrophic event is of great comparative interest. It also suggests a tensile rather than a compressive mechanism.

Seismologists emphasize the limitations of such estimates due to the numerous assumptions introduced. The Kolar gold field records above were obtained from a seismograph damped to record only a limited range of amplitude and rockbursts above this range displaced the stylus. A comparison of those recorded with the effects of those of greater amplitude, left the impression that energy greatly in excess of the above orders would be involved in the heaviest rockbursts. These were cyclic in their occurrence with intervals of several years between them. This invites the suggestion of a gradual accumulation of strain energy with mining until through some failure mechanism, it is suddenly released.

In a perfectly elastic body strain energy is accumulated in accordance with the following formula:

$$S = \frac{1}{2E} \{P_x^2 + P_y^2 + P_z^2 - 2\gamma\, (P_x P_y + P_y P_z + P_z P_x)\}$$

S = strain energy

E = Young's modulus

γ = Poisson's ratio

P_x, P_y, and P_z = principal stresses

Insofar as stress is proportional to strain, strain energy is immediately recoverable on removal of load. However, some strain energy is consumed in any plastic deformation. Plasticity is thus a factor limiting rockburst potential. The unit free energy content of rocks at failure depends upon the conditions of failure. Also the volume of rock involved in significant stress changes as a result of failure, in any particular case, is largely a matter of opinion. In spite of these very severe limitations any explanation of the rockburst phenomena must be capable of providing a wide range of available energy (103, 107).

In a search for the energy of rockbursts the high energy release possible with shear failure suggests some priority for that mechanism. In practice, tensile stresses are usually relieved by the opening of joint planes and a loosening of the rock mass. When this possibility is retarded by friction resulting from an intermediate principal stress, accumulating strain could be relieved by sudden failure, following any of the patterns of figure 54. Rockbursts located deep in the walls of large stoping areas (102) are probably due to tensile strains.

A further failure possibility, referred to in figure 53, should not be overlooked. Any subsidence at surface, as a result of an underground excavation represents the dissipation of potential energy. Some of this could be liberated through rockbursts (103).

Finally the types of failure shown in figures 14 and 15, though most characteristic of the laboratory, require consideration in a rockburst context. Rising stress at the face due to increasing span may be modified by "free-shear" failure ahead of the face or by tensile failure in the walls. To this degree the two mechanisms are in competition. Until there is a better understanding of the role of each mechanism in the rockburst context, it would be unwise to discount the tensile possibility.

Classification

In spite of possible inaccuracies, the energy of the seismic disturbance is the best indication of the magnitude of rockbursts, but it tells little of the physical factors involved. Fracture, relaxing, and stress zones have been referred to. There is a departure from the normal or gradual development of these zones when their spheres of influence reach towards radically different ground conditions, structural irregularities, or pillar loading. In each case stress trajectories are diverted, leading to the gradual or sudden adjustment of all three zones to re-establish equilibrium.

With elastic conditions predominating it is thus reasonable to assume that a rockburst is a possibility whenever the variables controlling the development of these zones are such as to demand a revision in their normal outlines or the merging of two or more sets of zones. On this basis, the following classification for rockbursts can be justified in practice: rockbursts related to a single opening; rockbursts related to geological structure; rockbursts related to pillar structures.

THE SINGLE OPENING

This category covers development headings, rooms, chambers, and single-stoping areas being mined by longwalling or its modifications without rigid pillar support at any depth and beyond the influence of other mining activity. It implies apparently normal conditions as regards structure and stress distribution and thus includes those rockbursts which occur for no obvious reason and which sometimes only interrupt the rhythm of gradual failure.

The causes can be attributed to inherent strains related to tectonics or earlier loading history of the rock mass, to time effects, and to the many factors which can vary strength-stress ratios locally, such as changes in rock properties or stress concentrations. The causes also may be associated with "free-shear" at the working face, figure 45, or tension as in figure 54. Fortunately type 1 rockbursts are very local in their effects, and modern supporting facilities provide for substantial protection.

GEOLOGICAL STRUCTURE

As experience with an orebody develops, a relationship between rockbursts and certain geological features may become apparent. The writer is aware of a single fault line, one of several in the vicinity, where over a range of several thousand vertical feet, a development heading on approaching this fault could be expected to burst. This could be due to strains related to the faulting or to weakness in the rock developed as a result of the faulting.

A classical example of the effect of a discontinuity is illustrated in figures 108 to 111 which show in plan, in longitudinal, and in cross-section a stoping area dipping at about 80° and cut off on one side by a large, nearly vertical diabase dike crossing the lode line at 65°. Stoping commenced at various levels towards the middle of the ore run, figure 108, without the benefit of any predetermined sequence. In this process with the short strike length involved, it is assumed, with some confirmation from crosscuts, figure 109, that normal fracture zones developed in the hangingwall and footwall as shown by the broken lines on the plan, figure 110. When stoping reached the dike on most of the levels, strains had developed which caused rupture along the footwall contact of the dike over a vertical range of some 400 feet, figure 111, resulting in the enlarged and final fracture zone of figure 110. This outline also has some corroboration from crosscuts and from an inspection of the ruptured contact on various levels.

The rupture along the contact took the form of a rather heavy rockburst. It forced the footwall some 18 inches into the unit-supported stoping excavation for some distance on strike from the dike contact. The hangingwall fracture zone appeared to be unaffected by this footwall rockburst. Had stoping proceeded outwards from the dike contact in sequence either from the top down or from the bottom upwards, the initial fracture zones, from its commencement, could have taken the form of the final fracture zone, involving no radical change in outline during the course of mining and thus no rockburst.

Regardless of the direction of a major discontinuity, if it is brought within the range of the stress redistribution associated with a mining excavation, stress concentrations can be expected as a result. Under some conditions a rockburst may follow.

At the other extreme the effect of a zone or zones of abnormal strength require consideration. Rockbursts or bumps have been associated with geological successions where one or more of the hangingwall members have been of greater than average strength. Such cases, referred to earlier, are on record from both coal (106) and potash mines (105). In the latter case, pillar structures also were involved. The mechanics of failure in both cases is a matter of opinion and difficult to discuss outside of the actual operational context.

With caving operations, inducing the initial cave has been known to result in the sudden failure of substantial tonnages of ore, yet subsequent operations proceeded with great regularity. Geometry, no doubt, has a place in such phenomena.

A type of rockburst described in South Africa as related to the fracture zone

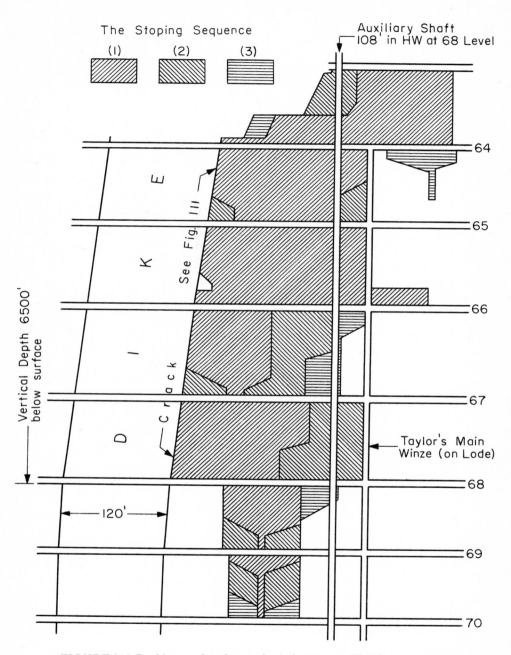

FIGURE 108 Rockburst related to geological structure. The Ooregum Mine, South India

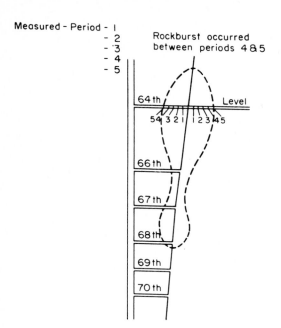

FIGURE 109 Section through auxiliary shaft, Ooregum Mine

FIGURE 111 This crack extends for 400 feet, vertical, along the Dike Schist contact. Ref., figure 108

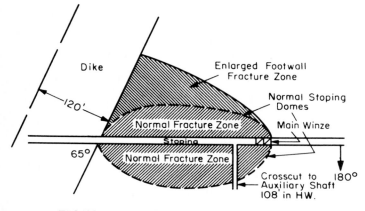

FIGURE 110 Generalized level plan

also can be included in this category. It is assumed to be caused by the failure of a Voussoir arch structure built up of ruptured material within the fracture zone. These bursts are regarded as less violent than those due to the rupture *in situ* of solid rock. They could represent the lower energy release of tensile failure in the solid.

PILLAR STRUCTURES

This heading covers the general case of pillars when sudden failure results in the merging of two or more sets of compression, relaxing, and fracture zones. It includes the cases of shaft and barrier pillars, of stoping in parallel and branching veins, of stoping in the vicinity of other openings, and of the effects of pillar failure in rigid pillar mining. The condition is associated with the zone of increasing strain energy shown in figure 91.

The typical case of the complete failure of a single pillar is illustrated in figure 112. This shows a pillar structure with initial relaxing and fracture zones over each stoping excavation. When the pillar is mined, or through rupture ceases to act as a rigid support, the initial fracture and relaxing zones merge into an adjusted state of equilibrium. A large volume of rock "B" stands between the two conditions. While the pillar is an effective rigid support it is subjected to the high stress concentrations associated with such structures. When the pillar ceases to be an effective support, through either gradual or sudden failure, stress trajectories have been diverted to relax volume "B" and thus to merge the hangingwall and footwall fracture and relaxing zones to cover the increased span. Accumulated strain energy is dissipated in the process.

One cannot be dogmatic about the mechanisms resulting in pillar failure as they will vary with layout, structure, and rock properties as related to critical stresses in either tension or compression. Except for the effects of the tensile phases of the minor principal stresses in figures 35, 37, and 39, pillars are likely to fail from their surfaces inwards. This failure, in the first instance, is probably related to the "free-shear" mechanism described earlier, which in turn, also reduces the effective pillar area.

"Free-shear" failures have seismic repercussions but the stage at which they reach the rockburst range is a matter of opinion. It is suggested that in the transition of volume "B", Figure 112 from rigidity to rupture, "free-shear" is progressive to the point where simple shear in the pillar core completes the failure process and stress trajectories are effectively shifted to more rigid areas.

At any stage in the above progression "free-shear" and / or simple shear may appear as gradual or sudden phenomena. In the latter event the magnitude of the seismic activity would be the criterion for inclusion in the rockburst category.

Control Measures

The major variables contributing to rock failure, gradual or sudden are as follows: the pre-mining stress distribution; the structure and properties of the rock mass; the support and geometry of excavations.

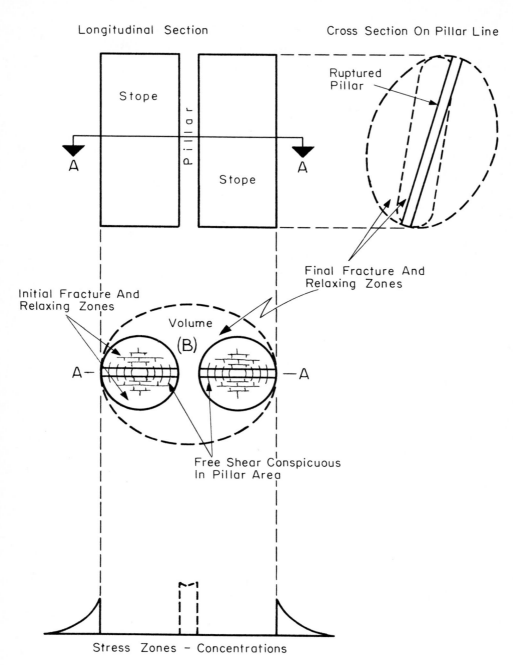

FIGURE 112 Zones merging with pillar failure

For a particular orebody the first two are facts which must be accepted. This leaves only support and geometry as subject to varying degrees of control.

SUPPORT

As ground is mined stress trajectories are shifted to bypass the excavation. Regardless of the type of support, this implies some adjustment to compression, relaxing, and fracture zones and accordingly rockbursts have continued in spite of the best supporting practice.

In general, support must be capable of yielding sufficiently to avoid its own destruction under both static and dynamic loading. It can influence rockburst incidence only insofar as it can resist changes in compression, relaxing, and fracture zones. Thus rigid support can be effective only within the range of its strength in compression. On the other hand, with filling methods the increasing resistance as spans are extended retards changes in these various zones. This limits the ground exposed to rockburst incidence and dampens any seismic activity generated with rockbursts elsewhere. The best results will be obtained with the earliest placement of fill which can be retained in place during subsequent mining.

GEOMETRY

With the contribution of support limited, for a reduction in the incidence of rockbursts we must rely on our knowledge of the effects of the geometry of openings, and of structural discontinuities on the concentration of stresses.

In development headings the beneficial effects of geometry can be obtained by cutting openings to shapes to which they normally would arch or burst. This implies some knowledge of the ground and, with stoping, limits possibilities to the plane of the lode. Thus for rockbursts related to a single opening, while supporting practice may buy time, with mining already on a longwall sequence the possibility of a further reduction in rockburst incidence is not good.

Rockbursts related to geological structure and to pillar structure are the most prolific and destructive occurrences. They are related to extremes in stress concentrations which, in turn, are related to geometry and / or structure and to that degree are amenable to some control.

In rockburst country, experience associates rockbursts with pillar structures to such a degree that the best solution is to eliminate the order of mining that demands their formation. This represents the application of the sequential longwall principle, figure 62.

The fullest initial development of an area permits the best layout. This will provide that shafts, haulages, hoisting and pumping installations, and other key openings are suitably located with respect to structure and to the stress redistribution that will follow with stoping.

The stoping sequence, preferably retreating, must take note of major structural features, preclude the formation of pillars and remnants with their high stress concentrations, and in general offer the earliest opportunity for the gradual failure of the rock mass involved.

The sequence for branching and closely parallel orebodies should be related in such a way that stoping in one, preferably the hangingwall, is well in advance of stoping in the other. Ideally the mining of the second orebody should commence in and extend the relaxing or fracture zone developed with the first stoping. The preference for the hangingwall in the first mining is to ensure that in open stopes the walls can move only inwards, but with an efficient filling operation this specification could give way to other considerations.

If such a sequence is introduced with the initial stoping the development of only a single fracture and relaxing zone in each wall is possible. This results in the least possible variation in stress concentrations from the beginning to the end of the operation. If a retreating sequence is provided, level maintenance usually is confined to the zone of increased stress on the periphery of the stoping excavation.

As noted earlier, the successful application of longwall methods depends upon the existence of a state of incipient failure at the working face and elsewhere on the periphery of the mined area. This condition does not exist when gradual failure, stabilizing the rock mass, does not follow the advance of the face and under such conditions rockbursts have occurred. In most cases they are very local in their effects. Occasionally their focus was so remote from operations that effects were not apparent. In a few serious cases involving complicated geometry large areas of mines have been rendered inaccessible. In such cases with unit supports, a solution might well require either filling or pillar support between limited longwall spans to a degree which eliminates the possibility of economic operations. With the steeper dips and the more limited extent of metalliferous orebodies, this problem is unusual in longwall mining when filling follows close behind the working face.

DE-STRESSING

Rockburst incidence is frequently increased during the blasting cycle and de-stressing holes are designed to extend this effect. Such holes have been drilled and blasted well beyond the effects of routine blasting on both development and stoping faces. The immediate objective is to extend the distance between the stress zone and the face. In doing so it would ease the problem of intermittent zone development and, in the case of pillars, it might induce sufficient movement within the structure to de-stress the pillar.

Where the method has been tried the psychological effects have been favourable but the stress changes resulting are less certain. Statistical studies are available from South Africa (13) indicating a decrease in rockburst incidence and severity as a result of the practice, but more recent work is less optimistic (108). No doubt one of the stress-measuring techniques ultimately will be used to determine stress changes, if any, resulting from the practice.

Summary and Conclusions

Deteriorating ground conditions usually are reflected in gradual and progressive ground failure in and around mining excavations. As the progress generally is predictable, the associated risks are essentially economic and thus, within the range of profit, may be tolerable. The cause of the conditions, all too often, is regarded as "naturally bad" ground; that the conditions might be man-made is frequently overlooked.

Due to their unpredictable nature rockbursts are at the other extreme and, unfortunately, carry a risk to personnel. They are likely to occur when the more elastic rock types are exposed to high stress concentrations, usually associated with pillar structures and structural discontinuities. The most prolific rockburst areas are probably under great tectonic strain and the mechanics of the problem appear to be closely related to the decompression of the rock mass exposed by mining. This suggests that effective support should provide a solution but experience has shown that no supporting practice can effectively prevent the shifting of stress trajectories as mining progresses. Thus, good supporting practice in resisting static and dynamic loading may reduce the volume of rock failure, but it contributes little to a reduction in rockburst incidence.

Geometry resulting in high stress concentrations can be avoided by a longwall sequence of stope faces which is suitably orientated for structural conditions and which also eliminates the need for pillars and projecting remnants with their extremes in stress concentration. The mining layout also must provide that key openings are located with due regard for the stress redistribution that follows with stoping. Such longwall sequences inducing the most moderate stress changes are the important contribution in controlling the effects of compression but under some conditions of loading, with tension and compression in competition, a limiting factor could be a maximum span beyond which tensile effects, as in Figure 54, could operate to result in rockbursts.

There is no absolute solution to the rockburst problem. In de-stressing a large volume of rock, under high compression prior to mining, some bursting is to be expected. However a tolerable control is possible by the use of a rigorous mining sequence. Then the next priority — the security of travelling ways — also becomes a possibility.

References

(1) Rock Mechanics Research. National Academy of Science, National Research Council, Washington, D.C. Publication 1466, 1966.

(2) D. F. Coates. Rock Mechanics Principles. Mines Branch Monograph 874 (revised 1970). Department of Energy, Mines and Resources. Ottawa, Ontario.

(3) L. Obert and W. I. Duvall. Rock Mechanics and the Design of Structures in Rock. John Wiley & Sons Inc. New York, 1967.

(4) D. F. Coates and M. Gyenge. Incremental Design in Rock Mechanics. Mines Branch 880, 1973. Department of Energy, Mines and Resources. Ottawa, Ontario.

(5) A. Salustowicz. New Conceptions as to the Phenomena of Stresses and Strains around Mining Excavations. International Strata Control Congress. Leipzig, 1958.

(6) R. Howink. Elasticity, Plasticity and Structure of Matter. Dover Publications Inc. New York, 1958.

(7) R. G. K. Morrison and D. F. Coates. Soil Mechanics Applied to Rock Failure in Mines. *Transactions Canadian Institute of Mining and Metallurgy*, 58 (1955):401–11.

(8) Bureau of Mines Test Procedure for Rocks. United States Bureau of Mines IC 8628, 1974.

(9) M. Reiner. Phenomenological Macrorheology, Rheology, vol. 1. Academic Press Inc., 1956.

(10) K. Terzaghi. Theoretical Soil Mechanics. New York: John Wiley & Sons, Inc., 1951.

(11) A. Nadai. Theory of Flow and Fracture of Solids, vol. 1. McGraw Hill Book Company, Inc. New York, 1963.

(12) D. W. Philips. Tectonics of Mining. *Colliery Engineering,* June, August, September, October and November, 1948.

(13) H. G. Denkhaus, F. G. Hill and A. J. A. Roux. Review of Research into Rockbursts and Strata Movement in Deep Level Mining in South Africa. *Institute of Mining and Metallurgy Bulletin.* April, 1959.

(14) McGill Laboratory Tests.

(15) E. L. Cameron. M. Eng. Thesis. McGill University, 1953.

(16) W. D. Ortlepp. M. Eng. Thesis. McGill University, 1957.

(17) J. J. L. Davies. M. Eng. Thesis. McGill University, 1959.

(18) A. A. Griffiths. The Theory of Rupture. Proceedings First International Congress for Applied Mathematics. Delft, 1924. *Philosophical Transactions,* Royal Society, London, vol. 221, pp. 163-98. 1921, Series A.

(19) McClintock and Walsh. Friction on Griffiths Cracks under Pressure. International Congress on Applied Mechanics. Berkeley, 1962.

(20) D. T. Griggs. Experimental Flow in Rocks under Conditions Favouring Recrystallization. *Geological Society of America* 51 (1940):1012.

(21) E. Orowan. Fracture and Strength of Solids. *Reports on Progress in Physics* 12 (1949):185-232.

(22) P. S. B. Colback. The Influence of Moisture Content in the Compressive Strength of Rocks. Unpublished.

(23) R. W. Goranson. Flow in Stressed Solids — An Interpretation. *Geological Society of America* 51 (1940):1026.

(24) D. T. Griggs. Deformation of Rocks under High Confining Pressure. *Journal of Geology* 44, no. 5 (1936):561.

(25) Investigation of Mining Subsidence Phenomena. *National Coal Board, Bulletin* 52 / 78 (1952).

(26) R. J. Orchard. Surface Effects of Mining — The Main Factors. *Colliery Guardian,* 9 August 1956.

(27) J. E. Marr. The Estimation of Mining Subsidence. *Colliery Guardian,* 19 March 1959.

(28) Investigation of Mining Subsidence Phenomena. *National Coal Board, Bulletin* 63 / 240 (1963).

(29) J. Tuzo Wilson. Continental Drift. *Scientific American* (April 1963): 86-100. J. R. Heirtzler. Sea-Floor Spreading. *Scientific American* (December 1968): 60-70.

(30) E. Tincelin. Research on Rock Pressures in the Iron Mines of Lorraine (France). International Conference about Rock Pressure and Support in Workings. Liege, 1951.

(31) O. J. Olsen. Measurement of Residual Stress by the Strain Relief Method. *Colorado School of Mines Quarterly* 52, no. 3 (1957).

(32) E. R. Leeman. The Measurement of Stress in Rock. *Transactions South African Institute of Mining and Metallurgy* 65, no. 2 (September 1964) and no. 4 (November 1964).

(33) C. L. Emery. Measurement of Strains in Mine Rocks. Symposium on Mining. Missouri School of Mines. Rolla, Missouri, 1961.

(34) L. Obert, R. H. Merrill and T. A. Morgan. Borehole Deformation Gauge for Determining the Stress on Mine Rock. United States Bureau of Mines R.I. 5978, 1962.

(35) A. N. May. The Measurement of Rock Pressure Induced by Mineral Extraction. *Transactions Canadian Institute of Mining and Metallurgy* 63 (1960):498-504.

(36) E. L. J. Potts. Underground Instrumentation. *Colorado School of Mines Quarterly* 52, no. 3 (1957).

(37) Nils Hast. The Measurement of Rock Pressure in Mines. Sveriges Geologiska Undersokning. Arsbok 52 no. 3, 1958, Stockholm.

(38) A. Roberts et al. A Laboratory Study of the Photoelastic Stress Meter. *International Journal of Rock Mechanics and Mining Sciences* 1, no. 3 (May 1964):441–58.

(39) Robert H. Merrill et al. Stress Determinations by Flat Jack and Borehole Deformation Methods. United States Bureau of Mines RI 6400, 1964.

(40) L. A. Panek and J. A. Stock. Development of a Rock Stress Monitoring Station Based on the Flat Slot Method of Measuring Existing Rock Stresses. United States Bureau of Mines RI 6537, 1964.

(41) Symposium on Rock Mechanics and Strata Control in Mines; April 1963 — June 1965. *Transactions South African Institute of Mining and Metallurgy*, 1965.

(42) G. Herget. Ground Stress Determinations in Canada. Internal Report 73 / 128, Mining Research Center, Mines Branch, Department of Energy, Mines and Resources. For Twenty-second Geo-Mechanics Conference. Salzburg, 1973.

(43) G. Herget. Stress Determinations in the Sudbury Area. Part I. Doorstopper and Triaxial Strain Cell Tests. Divisional Report MRL 75-22, CANMET, EMR. Ottawa, Canada. Feb. 1975.

(44) M. D. G. Salamon, J. A. Ryder and W. D. Ortlepp. An Analogue Solution for Determining the Elastic Response of Strata Surrounding Tabular Mining Excavations. *Transactions South African Institute of Mining and Metallurgy* 65, no. 2 (September 1964).

(45) W. D. Ortlepp and A. Nicoll. The Elastic Analysis of Observed Strata Movement by Means of an Electrical Analogue. *Transactions South African Institute of Mining and Metallurgy* 65, no. 4 (November 1964).

(46) L. Obert. Effects of Stress Relief and Other Changes in Stress in the Physical Properties of Rocks. United States Bureau of Mines RI 6053. 1962.

(47) Y. S. Yu and D. F. Coates. The Development and Use of Computer Programs for Finite Element Analysis. Research Report R198. Mining Research Center. Department of Energy, Mines and Resources, Ottawa, Canada. July 1969.

(48) W. I. Duvall. Stress Analysis Applied to Underground Mining Problems, parts I and II. United States Bureau of Mines, RI 4192, 4387. 1948.

(49) L. Obert, W. I. Duvall and R. H. Merrill. Design of Underground Openings in Competent Rock. *United States Bureau of Mines Bulletin* 587 (1960).

(50) H. G. Denkhaus. The Application of the Mathematical Theory of Elasticity to Problems of Stress in Hard Rocks at Great Depths. Association of Mine Mangers of South Africa, 1958.

(51) K. Terzaghi and F. E. Richart Jr. Stress in Rock about Cavities. *Geotechnique* 3 (1952).

(52) L. Panek. Stresses about Mine Openings in a Homogeneous Rock Body. Ann Arbor, Mich: Edwards Bros. Inc., 1953.

(53) L. P. Geldart and J. E. Udd. Boundary Stresses around an Elliptical Opening in an Infinite Elastic Medium. First Canadian Symposium on Rock Mechanics. McGill University, 7 and 8 September, 1962.

(54) G. Kirsch. Die Theorie de Elastizitat Und Die Bedurfnisse Der Festigkeitslehre Vereines. *Deutscher Ingenieure Journal* 42, no. 29 (16 July 1898):797–807. Sonnabend.

(55) M. A. Mahtab. A Study of the Field Stress Distribution around an Elliptical Hole under Different Loading Conditions. M. Eng. Thesis. McGill, 1965.

(56) B. B. Dhar. Stresses in Depth around an Oval Opening in an Elastic Medium. M. Eng. Thesis. McGill, 1966.

(57) B. B. Dhar, L. P. Geldart, and J. E. Udd. Stresses in Depth Around Elliptical and Ovaloidal Openings in an Infinite Elastic Medium. *Transactions Canadian Institute of Mining and Metallurgy* 73 (1970).

(58) R. G. K. Morrison and L. P. Geldart. Rock Stresses Induced by Block Caving. *Transactions Canadian Institute of Mining and Metallurgy* 67 (1964):71–73.

(59) R. G. K. Morrison and L. P. Geldart. Rock Stresses Induced by Shrinkage Stoping. *Transactions Canadian Institute of Mining and Metallurgy,* 67 (1964):92–94.

(60) J. E. Udd and O. B. Nair. Stresses around Openings in a Plate Due to Biaxial Load through a Superpositioning Technique. Third Canadian Rock Mechanics Symposium. University of Toronto, January 1965.

(61) J. C. Jaeger and N. G. W. Cook. Pinching Off and Discing of Rock. *Journal of Geophysical Research* 68, no. 6 (15 March 1963):1759–65.

(62) A. J. Rambosek. The Stress Field within a Core Stub in a Bore Hole. United States Bureau of Mines RI 6462. 1964.

(63) L. Obert and D. E. Stephenson. Stress Conditions under Which Core Discing Occurs. *Transactions Society of Mining Engineers,* AIME (Sept. 1965):227–35.

(64) A. J. Duralli, L. Obert and V. J. Parks. Stress Required to Initiate Discing. *Transactions American Institute of Mining Engineers* 241, no. 3, pp. 269–76.

(65) M. Barcza and G. R. P. Von Willich. Strata Movements at Harmony Gold Mine. Papers of Mine Managers Association of South Africa. 1958.

(66) F. G. Hill and H. G. Denkhaus. Rock Mechanics Research in South Africa with Special Reference to Rockbursts and Strata Movement in Deep Level Gold Mines. Seventh Commonwealth Mining and Metallurgical Congress, South Africa, 1961.

(67) D. F. Coates. Pillar Loading, Parts, 1, 2, 3, and 4. (Mines Branch Research Reports, Nos. 168, 170, 180 and 193). Department of Energy, Mines and Resources. Ottawa, Ontario, 1965 and 1966.

(68) R. G. K. Morrison, A. V. Corlett and H. R. Rice. *Ontario Department of Mines Bulletin* 155, part 2 (1961).

(69) D. G. F. Hedley and F. Grant. Stope and Pillar Design for the Elliot Lake Uranium Mines. *Transactions Canadian Institute of Mining and Metallurgy* 75 (1972):121–28.

(70) Charles T. Holland. Coal Mine Pillars for Permanent and Semipermanent Support of the Overburden. Ninth Canadian Symposium on Rock Mechanics. Ecole Polytechnique, Montreal, Dec. 1973.

(71) M. D. G. Salamon. A Method of Designing Bord and Pillar Workings. *Journal South African Institute of Mining and Metallurgy* (Sept. 1967).

(72) M. D. G. Salamon and A. H. Munro. A Study of the Strength of Coal Pillars. *Journal South African Institute of Mining and Metallurgy* (September 1967).

(73) A. J. Bieniawski. The Effect of Specimen Size on the Strength of Coal. *International Journal Rock Mechanics and Mineral Science* (1967), pp. 325–35.

(74) A. H. Wilson and O. P. Ashwin. Research into the Determination of Pillar Size, parts 1 and 2. *Transactions Institute of Mining and Metallurgy* (June 1972), p. 141.

(75) R. H. Merrill. Design of Underground Mine Openings. Oil Shale Mine, Rifle, Colo. United States Bureau of Mines RI 5089. 1954.

(76) R. H. Merrill. Roof Span Studies in Limestone. United States Bureau of Mines RI 5348. 1957.

(77) R. H. Merrill and T. A. Morgan. Method of Determining the Strength of a Mine Roof. United States Bureau of Mines RI 5406. 1958.

(78) L. Obert and R. H. Merrill. A Review of Design Factors. Oil Shale Mine, Rifle, Colorado. United States Bureau of Mines RI 5429. 1958.

(79) I. F. C. Statham, ed. Coal Mining Practice. The Caxton Publishing Company Limited. 1958.

(80) C. B. Jeppe. Gold Mining of The Witwatersrand. Transvaal Chamber of Mines. Johannesburg, South Africa. 1946.

(81) M. A. Twidale. Backfill Methods in Canadian Mines. I. C. 141, Mines Branch, Department of Mines and Technical Surveys. Ottawa, Ontario. 1962.

(82) J. McCreedy and W. S. Taylor. The Use of Hydraulic Fill Underground at the Mines of the International Nickel Company of Canada Limited. *Canadian Mining Journal* (September 1960).

(83) Hydraulic Backfilling, Kerr-Addison Gold Mines Limited, Virginiatown, Ontario. *The Canadian Mining Journal* (May 1959).

(84) F. E. Patton. Backfilling at Noranda. *Transactions Canadian Institute of Mining and Metallurgy* 55 (1952):137–43.

(85) W. S. Weaver and R. Luka. Laboratory Studies of Cement-Stabilized Mine Tailings. *Transactions Canadian Institute of Mining and Metallurgy* 73 (1970):204–17.

(86) J. McCreedy and R. J. Hall. Cemented Sand Fill at The International Nickel Company. Canadian Institute of Mining and Metallurgy Annual Meeting. April 1966.

(87) P. C. McLeod and A. Schwartz. Consolidated Fill at Noranda Mines Limited (Geco Division). *Transactions Canadian Institute of Mining and Metallurgy* 73 (1970):227–34.

(88) Powered Supports. National Coal Board, *Information Bulletin* 62 / 239 (1962).

(89) A. Wright. Operational Problems of Support on Mechanized Coal Faces in The United Kingdom. International Strata Control Conference. Columbia University. New York, 1964.

(90) Georgius Agricola. De Re Metallica. Translated by H. C. and L. H. Hoover. Dover Publications Inc. New York, 1950.

(91) J. E. Belford. The Evolution of Rotary Drilling at Kidd Creek Mine. First Annual Underground Operators' Conference. Sudbury, Ontario. 25–28 Feb. 1975. (C.I.M., Montreal, Que.)

(92) N. A. Creet and W. J. Taylor. Blast Hole Drilling at The International Nickel Company of Canada, Limited, Ontario Division. First Annual Underground Operators' Conference. Sudbury, Ontario. 25–28 Feb., 1975. (C.I.M., Montreal, Que.)

(93) R. S. Cleland and K. H. Singh. Development of Post Pillar Mining at Falconbridge Nickel Mines Limited. *Canadian Institute of Mining and Metallurgy Bulletin* (April 1973).

(94) J. A. Pigott and R. J. Hall. Undercut and Fill Mining at the Frood-Stobie Mine of the International Nickel Company. *Transactions Canadian Institute of Mining and Metallurgy* 64 (1961):251–55. Also *AIME* 1962.

(95) H. Zorychta and G. S. Merrill. Load on Friction Props on a Longwall Face. *Transactions Canadian Institute of Mining and Metallurgy* 68 (1965):48–54.

(96) L. Janelid and R. Kvapil. Sublevel Caving. *International Journal of Rock Mechanics and Mineral Science* 3, no. 2 (May 1966).

(97) Amil Dubnie. Mining Technology Statistics 1972 and 1973. Department of Energy, Mines and Resources, *Technical Bulletin* 188. Ottawa, Ontario.

(98) R. G. K. Morrison. Report on the Rockburst Situation in Ontario Mines. *Transactions Canadian Institute of Mining and Metallurgy* 45 (1942).

(99) W. Blake, F. Leighton and W. I. Duvall. Microseismic Techniques For Monitoring The Bahaviour Of Rock Structures. United States Bureau of Mines, Bulletin 665 (1974).

(100) Y. P. Aggarwal et al. Premonitory Changes in Seismic Velocities and Prediction of Earthquakes. *Nature* 241, no. 5385 (12 Jan. 1973). Also Frank Press, *Scientific American* (May 1975).

(101) J. S. Jones. Discussion Notes on Ground Movement and Methods of Support in Deep Mining. P. J. Crowle, *Kolar Gold Field Mining and Metallurgy Society* 4 (1927–28):69.

(102) P. G. Gane, A. L. Hales and H. O. Oliver. A Seismic Investigation of Witwatersrand Earth Tremors. *Bulletin Seismological Society of America* 36, no. 2 (April 1946).

(103) N. G. W. Cook. The Basic Mechanics of Rockbursts. *Transactions South African Institute of Mining and Metallurgy* 64, no. 3 (October 1973).

(104) D. F. Coates. Energy Released in Rockbursts. *Colorado School of Mines Quarterly* 54, no. 3 (1959).

(105) G. Spackeler et al. New Data on Rockbursts in Potash Mines. International Conference on Strata Control. Paris, 1960.

(106) Report of The Royal Commission Appointed to Inquire into the Upheaval or Fall or Other Disturbances Sometimes Referred to as a Bump in No. 2 Mine at Springhill in the County of Cumberland, N.S. Operated by the Cumberland Railway & Coal Company on 23 October 1958.

(107) N. G. W. Cook. A Note on Rockbursts Considered as a Problem of Stability. *Journal South African Institute of Mining and Metallurgy* 65, no. 8 (March 1965).

(108) N. G. W. Cook et al. Rock Mechanics Applied to the Study of Rockbursts. *Journal South African Institute of Mining and Metallurgy* 66, no. 10 (May 1966).

(109) M. H. Dickhout. Ground Control at the Creighton Mine of the International Nickel Company of Canada Limited, First Canadian Rock Mechanics Symposium. McGill University, 1962. Information Canada, Ottawa, 1963.

Index